Seniors Save Money

All Year Around

Through All Kinds of Discounts, Free Offers and Valuable Information

For People 50+ in Edmonton & Area

by

**Alberta Business Research Ltd.,
publisher of the *Edmonton Senior* newspaper with
research and writing by Denise Daubert.**

Published by   Alberta Business Research Ltd.
200, 10621-100 Avenue
Edmonton, Alberta
Canada T5J 0B3
(780) 429-1610

While we believe the information in this book is accurate at the time of compilation, this is not guaranteed, and discounts, websites and other data may change over time. This book provides general information and neither Alberta Business Research Ltd. nor its employees render professional, medical, health, legal or financial advice, nor are they responsible or liable for any injury, illness or loss resulting or alleged to be resulting from the information in this book.

Library and Archives Canada Cataloguing in Publication

Seniors save money all year around through all kinds of discounts, free offers and valuable information: for people 50+ in Edmonton and area/by Alberta Business Research Ltd., publishers of the *Edmonton Senior* and *Calgary Senior* newspapers; with research and writing by Denise Daubert.

Includes index.

ISBN 0-9692200-3-0

1.   Discounts for older people–Alberta–Edmonton–Handbooks, manuals, etc.

2.   Older people–Alberta–Edmonton–Finances, Personal–Handbooks, manuals, etc.

I.   Daubert, Denise II. Alberta Business Research Ltd.

HV1475.A5S46 2005   362.6'097123'34   C2005-906910-4

DIGITALLY PRINTED BY

Acknowledgements

The publisher would like to thank the editorial team of Alberta Business Research Ltd. and staff for the time spent and excellent work that has gone into *Seniors Save Money All Year Around Through All Kinds of Discounts, Free Offers and Valuable Information For People 50+ in Edmonton and Area.*

Those involved in this senior handbook project include:
Publisher – *Lorne Silverstein*
Editor – *Colin F. Smith*
Assistant Editor – *Jeannie Chua*
Research/Writing – *Denise Daubert*
Marketing – *Patricia MacDonald*
Fact Checking – *Janice Gosselin*

Special acknowledgements go to Denise Daubert, who spent many hours telephoning and researching this information, and writing this new publication. Thank you, Denise, for very thorough and detailed work on savings and discounts in Edmonton and area.

Table of Contents

Introduction

The area of saving money is multifaceted. We have therefore researched not only specific senior discounts but coupons, loyalty programs and offers that provide good value, and present these findings in this book.

The listings of merchants, stores, companies and services offering savings are by no means exhaustive. There certainly could be some other savings and offers that we did not come across or brand-new discounts that have just been introduced.

As it is impossible in a book this size to list all businesses that offer a senior discount, it is important that you ask about senior discounts every time you shop or use a service. Also keep in mind that some discounts or loyalty programs may be discontinued and that admission prices can increase from year to year.

The focus, of course, is on senior discounts and "Seniors' Day" promotions, through which you can save money on meals, entertainment, books, pet supplies and fitness, just to name a few possibilities. But in the "spirit of saving," this book also outlines some great loyalty programs, free activities and promotions that provide other ways of saving money.

Yellow page advertisements are great sources for discovering where the senior discounts are and who offers them. Also, some companies will give anyone a discount if you mention you saw their advertisement!

Customer Appreciation Programs

As ways of saving money, "Customer Appreciation Programs" and "Loyalty Programs" have become very popular with consumers during the last decade or so. It is important, however, that you carry your club cards with you and use them – have them swiped or stamped – each time you shop at an establishment. Customer Appreciation Programs usually provide discounts in the form of dollars off a purchase and Loyalty Programs usually enable customers to use points earned for travel, merchandise, movie tickets and so on.

Coverage Area

The City of Edmonton proper is surrounded by close-by communities and together they form what is known as the Capital Region. So this book includes comprehensive information for the communities of Sherwood Park to the east, St. Albert to the north, Spruce Grove and Stony Plain to the west and Leduc to the south.

Easy Reference

For easy reference, you will find boxed phrases throughout the book:

FREE

SAVE

GOOD VALUE

LOYALTY PROGRAM

PROMOTION

CUSTOMER APPRECIATION PROGRAM

INFORMATION

AFFORDABLE

Addresses, telephone numbers and websites are listed for you as well.

Lastly, to make it all the easier, listings are sorted by community and are alphabetized. For example, in Chapter 1, if you want to find "fine dining" restaurants in Edmonton and area that offer senior discounts or promotions, you can search by community (e.g. Edmonton, Sherwood Park and so on) under "Fine Dining," and then alphabetically by restaurant name.

Age Requirements

Most businesses specify the qualifying age for their seniors' discount – 50-plus, 65-plus etc. Some businesses, however, will grant a seniors' discount to anyone who appears to be a senior. In such cases, the term "Senior" appears under "Age Requirements."

The Importance of Asking

"Do you have a seniors' discount?"
"I'm a senior. Do you offer discounts to seniors?"

Never be shy about asking these questions. The worst anyone can say is "No." You've earned the chance to benefit from the multitude of senior discounts available out there! Sometimes when you ask, even if a restaurant or store does not normally offer a senior discount, they may provide one to you on the spot to keep your business. If enough seniors ask, a store or business that doesn't currently have a senior discount may start giving one.

Keep in mind that store clerks or restaurant employees may not think of informing you about their senior discount – you may not look old enough or the clerk or employee may forget to mention it because he or she is new at the job.

The Power of Coupons

Ah, coupons! Don't underestimate the savings in this area. For example, coupons can be applied to grocery purchases or to craft purchases and towards meals at restaurants. A couple of popular books containing valuable discount coupons are sold by non-profit groups and schools. See Chapter 11 for more information.

Envelopes containing coupons or coupon booklets may sometimes be delivered in the mail and can be found inserted in newspapers. Also, check the front of your telephone directory for

SuperPages coupons. You will find some great savings coupons from such companies as Art 'N Frame and Frame/Craft Picture Framing. You need to be aware that these SuperPages coupons have expiry dates, that you need to present the coupon upon purchase and also that advertisers and their offers can change from year to year. With all coupons, check for expiry dates.

On to Savings

Seniors Save Money All Year Around Through All Kinds of Discounts, Free Offers and Valuable Information For People 50+ in Edmonton & Area is brought to you by Alberta Business Research Ltd., which has been in business for 22 years and publishes the largest number of senior publications in Alberta, including the monthly *Edmonton Senior* newpaper. The newspaper is dedicated to keeping seniors 50-plus informed and connected!

Chapter 1

Food & Beverage

This chapter provides you with comprehensive information about where to find senior discounts and senior menus, plus restaurants at which diners with smaller appetites can order half-orders of entrees. These are all methods of "saving" when dining out.

In addition to information about Edmonton and area restaurants, this chapter provides information on grocery stores, bakeries, dessert factory outlets, farmers' markets and liquor stores.

Restaurants

There decidedly are many senior discounts available when dining out in Edmonton and the communities of Sherwood Park, St. Albert, Spruce Grove, Stony Plain and Leduc. There are many, many casual restaurants, buffets, Sunday brunches and fast-food places to choose from and they welcome the business of senior customers.

The following restaurant listings are by no means exhaustive. But we've done intensive research in this area of senior savings and provide you with what we've found. Remember, too, that there are always new senior discounts being added by restaurants, and if you ask, sometimes a restaurant that doesn't have a "set" senior discount will consider giving you one, to stay competitive.

Discounts and offers can change at any time, or even be discontinued, so keep that in mind, too.

It is important to note that generally, discounts offered pertain to purchases of a meal (food) only – beverages like coffee and soft drinks are sometimes excluded from the discount, and alcohol purchases are always excluded.

Watch your mailbox or for inserts in newspapers for coupons that can be redeemed at eating establishments. Also, see Chapter 11 (*Miscellaneous Discounts and Savings*) for information regarding the *Student Union Ticket Pak* and the *Entertainment Book* coupon books. A large portion of coupons in both are for restaurants in Edmonton and area, and make offers such as "buy one meal and get one free," "money off purchase," "free appetizers with any entrée order" or "free dessert."

Anyone (including seniors) can save by taking advantage of the multitude of breakfast specials or lunch specials offered by restaurants. Be aware that the times for these specials are pretty specific, so check before heading out. The prices on these specials are extremely good value. Also watch for periodic "all you can eat" specials that some restaurants offer during the year.

Some restaurants that do not offer a seniors' menu, with smaller portions and special pricing, will allow senior patrons to order from the lower-priced children's menu.

Restaurants have been listed by category (for example, "Bistros & Cafes" and "Sunday Brunches") for ease of reference. Restaurants that are located in Edmonton appear first in each category, followed by those in Sherwood Park, St. Albert, Spruce Grove, Stony Plain and Leduc respectively. The required age to benefit from a senior discount is clearly shown.

Bistros & Cafes

BISTROS & CAFÉS – EDMONTON

Café Europa

2nd level of Phase 3 at West Edmonton Mall; 444-5396

SAVE Seniors receive 15 per cent off the regular menu and senior pricing is offered on buffets, always.

Age Requirement: 65-plus

Café Select
- 10018 – 106 Street; 428-1629
- 8404 – 109 Street; 438-1812

SAVE For smaller appetites, the menu includes "lighter fare" items.
Age Requirement: Anyone

Chianti Café
10501 – 82 Avenue; 438-9829

SAVE Menu items can be prepared as half-orders for those with smaller appetites.
Age Requirement: Anyone

Grandma Lee's Bakery Café
Bonnie Doon Shopping Centre Food Court; 490-0382

SAVE Seniors save five per cent (excepting promotions).
Age Requirement: 65-plus

Urban Diner
- 12427 – 102 Avenue; 488-7274

SAVE Half-portions are available upon request.
Age Requirement: Anyone

Buffet Restaurants

BUFFET RESTAURANTS – EDMONTON

Buffet Royale
- 3318 – Gateway Boulevard; 439-8900
- 12866 Fort Road; 475-4600

SAVE $2 off for seniors lunch and dinner buffets all day Tuesday.
Age Requirement: 65-plus

Buffet World
- 13062 – 50 Street; 478-8889

SAVE $2 off for seniors lunch and dinner buffets on weekdays and $4 off for seniors lunch and dinner buffets on weekends.
Age Requirement: 55-plus

Royal Fork Buffet
- 15061 Stony Plain Road; 484-7025

CUSTOMER APPRECIATION PROGRAM Senior customers can join the "Senior Value Club" and have their card stamped each time they visit the lunch or dinner buffet and, after ten stamps, the 11th buffet is free of charge.
Age Requirement: 60-plus

Casino Restaurants

CASINO RESTAURANTS – EDMONTON

Casino Grill at The ABS Argyll Casino
- 7055 Argyll Road; 463-9467

SAVE Seniors receive a 10 per cent discount, always.
Age Requirement: 60-plus

Stagecoach Grill & Deli at The ABS Yellowhead Casino
- 12464 – 153 Street; 424-9467

SAVE Seniors receive a 10 per cent discount, always.
Age Requirement: 60-plus

Casual Dining

CASUAL DINING – EDMONTON

abc Country Restaurants
www.abccountry.ca
- 10804 – 170 Street; 484-2600
- 12707 – 140 Avenue; 456-7688
- 4485 Gateway Boulevard (in the Greenwood Inn); 436-5411

SAVE Both senior lunch and senior dinner menus offered, always.
Age Requirement: 60-plus

Albert's Family Restaurant
www.albertsfamilyrestaurants.com
- 132 Street and 137 Avenue; 456-6074
- 100 Avenue and 106 Street (in the Day's Inn); 413-4869
- 99 Street and 51 Avenue; 434-5577
- Bonnie Doon Shopping Centre; 466-6568
- Southgate Mall; 436-1784

- 9308 – 34 Avenue; 432-6664
- Abbotsfield Shopping Centre; 474-3344
- Capilano Shopping Centre; 469-5588
- Londonderry Shopping Centre; 473-2050
- West Edmonton Mall on Bourbon Street; 444-1179
- 124 Street and 106 Avenue; 488-9096
- 17620 – 100 Avenue (in the Comfort Inn); 489-2699
- 15540 Stony Plain Road (in the Howard Johnson Hotel); 489-3828

SAVE The "Club 55" senior menu is featured, plus there is a two-for-one special from the senior menu from 4 p.m. to close, Monday to Thursday (purchase of two beverages required for this special).
Age Requirement: 55-plus

Brewster's Restaurant
15820 – 87 Avenue; 421-4677
SAVE All-day senior menu offered.
Age Requirement: 55-plus

Cody's Restaurant
14915 Stony Plain Road; 443-3221
SAVE Senior menu offered, always.
Age Requirement: 60-plus

Denny's Restaurant
www.dennys.com
- 17635 Stony Plain Road; 487-3663
- 10803 – 104 Avenue; 425-8408
- 3604 Calgary Trail North; 438-3663
- 5021 – 25 Avenue; 450-3663

SAVE Senior breakfast, lunch and dinner menus offered, always.
INFORMATION You can substitute Egg Beaters for eggs at no charge. Sugar-free pancake syrup is available upon request.
Age Requirement: 55-plus

Fireside Restaurant
7240 – 118 Avenue; 471-3934
SAVE Senior menu offered, always.

INFORMATION This restaurant is located directly across from Rexall Place, so it is a perfect place to dine if you are going to a hockey game, concert or other event at Rexall Place.
Age Requirement: 65-plus

Flamingo Restaurant
- 15835 – 87 Avenue, 483-7178
- 2103 – 110 Street; 436-7942

SAVE Senior menu offered, always.
Age Requirement: 60-plus

Hap's Hungry House
16060 Stony Plain Road; 483-2288
SAVE Seniors may order off the Children's Menu, always.
Age Requirement: 65-plus

Humpty's Family Restaurant
www.humptys.com
- 4503 Gateway Boulevard; 430-9313
- 5011 – 130 Avenue; 476-8566
- 9910 – 108A Avenue; 429-3819
- 17006 – 90 Avenue; 487-6890
- 12503 – 127 Street; 488-2920
- 9555 – 82 Avenue; 437-0727
- 13232 – 97 Street; 478-2659
- 1320 Calgary Trail; 431-8006
- 7451 Roper Road; 485-2471

SAVE Ask for a membership card to the Humpty's Family Restaurant Emerald 55 Club at any of their locations – the club is free to join. There are two ways for seniors to save. Most menu items can be ordered one size smaller, as a smaller, lower-priced portion – similar to the restaurant's former senior menu but now with expanded choices. Seniors receive 20 per cent off their bill on Tuesdays and 10 per cent on other days.
Age Requirement: 55-plus

JB's Restaurant
3633 – 118 Avenue; 477-5885

`SAVE` Senior menu offered, always.
Age Requirement: 65-plus

Keegan's Restaurant (North Side)
12904 – 97 Street; 457-5590
`SAVE` Senior menu offered every day from 7 a.m. to 9 p.m. As well, during "Senior Evening," each Thursday between 3 and 9 p.m., buy one entree off the senior menu and get one entrée off the senior menu free; beverage purchase is required.
Age Requirement: 60-plus

Keegan's Restaurant (South Side)
8709 – 109 Street; 439-8034
`SAVE` Senior menu offered, always.
`INFORMATION` This is a 24-hour restaurant.
Age Requirement: 60-plus

Kelsey's Restaurant
- 320 Manning Crossing; 475-6880
- 9995 – 178 Street; 484-4770
- 13580 – 137 Avenue; 414-5807
- 11736 – 104 Avenue; 456-4476
`SAVE` Those with smaller appetites can order half-order entrees from the menu.
Age Requirement: Anyone

Lumber Jack Pancake & Steak House
- 8170 – 50 Street; 469-6702
- 5708 – 75 Street; 413-8388
`SAVE` Senior menu offered, always.
Age Requirement: 60-plus

Montana's Cookhouse
www.montanas.ca
38 Avenue and Calgary Trail; 434-2886
`SAVE` Smaller appetites may order off the Children's Menu anytime (beverages at regular price).
Age Requirement: Anyone

Muggn'z Family Restaurant
6655 – 178 Street; 487-5953
SAVE Senior menu offered, always.
Age Requirement: 55-plus

Poppa's Family Restaurant
4702 – 118 Avenue; 471-5749
SAVE Senior menu offered, always.
Age Requirement: 55-plus

Ricky's All Day Grill
www.rickys-restaurants.com
- 10140 – 109 Street; 421-7546
- 11431 Kingsway Avenue; 488-8238
- 9917 – 179 Street; 486-7109
- 10004 – 21 Avenue; 461-3011

SAVE Seniors can join the Golden Opportunity Club (enquire
at any of their locations; free to join) and receive a 10 per
cent discount from Tuesday to Sunday. The discount dou-
bles to 20 per cent on Mondays.

INFORMATION A Whyte Avenue location is opening soon.
Age Requirement: 55-plus

Roman's Family Restaurant
15815 Stony Plain Road; 444-2769
SAVE Senior dinner menu offered every day from 3 to 9 p.m.
Age Requirement: 60-plus

Rosie's At Argyll Plaza
6258 – 99 Street; 432-6942
SAVE Senior menu offered, every day. On Mondays, senior customers can "buy one and get one-half off" when ordering
from the regular menu.
Age Requirement: 65-plus

Smitty's
www.smittys.ca
- Westmount Shopping Centre; 452-2800
- Northgate Shopping Centre; 478-7731

- 18320 Stony Plain Road; 483-6457
- Kingsway Garden Mall; 479-1313
- Millwoods Towne Centre; 461-1825
- 137 Avenue and Manning Freeway; 408-5400
- 5359 Calgary Trail South; 434-8549

SAVE There is a senior all-day breakfast menu plus a senior lunch/dinner menu, every day.
Age Requirement: 60-plus

Smokey Joe's Hickory House
15135 Stony Plain Road; 413-3379
SAVE Senior menu offered, always.
Age Requirement: 65-plus

Teddy's Dining
11361 Jasper Avenue; 488-0984
SAVE Senior discount is 15 per cent, always.
Age Requirement: 65-plus

White Spot Restaurant
3921 Calgary Trail South; 432-9153
SAVE Senior customers can order from the Founder's Club menu, always.
Age Requirement: 55-plus

CASUAL DINING – SHERWOOD PARK

Albert's Family Restaurant
Sherwood Park Mall; 449-5029
See under Casual Dining – Edmonton.

Country Market Restaurant & Buffet
Yellowhead and Broadmoor Boulevard (at the Flying J Travel Centre); 416-2035
SAVE Seniors receive 10 per cent off both buffets and menu items, every day.
Age Requirement: 60+

Denny's Restaurant
975 Broadmoor Boulevard; 467-7893
See under Casual Dining – Edmonton.

Humpty's Family Restaurant
78, 975 Broadmoor Boulevard; 417-2867
See under Casual Dining – Edmonton.

Kelsey's Restaurant
42, 975 Broadmoor Boulevard; 417-3166
See under Casual Dining – Edmonton.

Montana's Cookhouse
2030 Sherwood Drive; 416-1870
See under Casual Dining – Edmonton.

CASUAL DINING – ST. ALBERT

Albert's Family Restaurant
Grandin Shopping Centre; 458-3826
See under Casual Dining – Edmonton.

Kelsey's Restaurant
300, 10 McKenney Avenue; 419-2933
See under Casual Dining – Edmonton.

Montana's Cookhouse
10, 445 St. Albert Road; 458-7770
See under Casual Dining – Edmonton.

Muggn'z Family Restaurant
388 St. Albert Road; 458-2046
See under Casual Dining – Edmonton.

Ricky's All-Day Grill
140 St. Albert Road; 418-0699
See under Casual Dining – Edmonton.

Smitty's
101, 375 St. Albert Road; 458-8808
See under Casual Dining – Edmonton.

CASUAL DINING – SPRUCE GROVE

Bing's Family Restaurant
21 Westway Road; 962-3997
SAVE Senior menu offered, always.

Age Requirement: 65-plus

Humpty's Family Restaurant
20, 100 Campsite Road; 960-4762
See under Casual Dining – Edmonton.

Ricky's All-Day Grill
70 McLeod Avenue; 960-5053
See under Casual Dining – Edmonton.

Smitty's
18 Westgrove Drive; 962-4866
See under Casual Dining – Edmonton.

CASUAL DINING – STONY PLAIN

abc Country Restaurant
#78 Boulder Boulevard; 968-5595
See under Casual Dining – Edmonton.

Backstreet Grill
4917 – 53 Avenue; 968-2578
SAVE Senior menu offered, always.
Age Requirement: 65-plus

Bing's Family Restaurant
5005 – 50 Street; 963-2609
SAVE Seniors can order off the Children's Menu. Half-orders of regular menu items are also available.
Age Requirement: 65-plus

Rainbow Palace Restaurant
93 McLeod Drive; 962-8388
SAVE Senior menu offered, always.
Age Requirement: 65-plus

Spiro's Family Dining
3303 – 43 Avenue; 963-0032
SAVE Senior menu offered, always.
Age Requirement: 55-plus

Rosie's Bar & Grill
8340 Sparrow Crescent; 986-7998

SAVE Seniors receive 10 per cent every day off regular menu items (does not include specials).
Age Requirement: 65-plus

Smitty's
5004 – 50 Avenue; 986-8923
See under Casual Dining – Edmonton.

White Spot Restaurant
5230 – 50 Avenue; 980-3484
See under Casual Dining – Edmonton.

Chinese Restaurants – Dine-in Buffets

There are several hundred small, medium-size and large Cantonese, Szechuan and other Chinese food establishments in Edmonton and surrounding areas. When dining in, senior discounts usually apply to their buffets. Check the multitude of advertisements in the yellow pages. Besides buffets, some of the restaurants listed here offer dine-in combination specials while others offer an order of wonton soup or dry ribs free with orders over a certain amount.

Beijing Beijing
3803 Calgary Trail; 430-7720

SAVE Seniors save 10 per cent on buffet dinners, every day.
Age Requirement: 65-plus

Good Taste Chinese Szechuan Cuisine
10933 – 23 Avenue (Heritage Square); 988-6633

SAVE Seniors receive a 10 per cent dine-in discount (except the special), on Monday and Tuesday evenings.
Age Requirement: 65-plus

Red Diamond House
7500 – 82 Avenue; 465-0755

SAVE Senior $12.95 for buffet Friday to Sunday evenings (Adult $13.95).
Age Requirement: 65-plus

Szechuan Castle
15415 – 111 Avenue; 484-6060
SAVE $2 off for seniors, evening buffet, every day.
Age Requirement: 65-plus

Smilie's Place (North End)
13022b – 82 Street; 478-2815
SAVE Seniors receive 10 per cent off all lunch and dinner buffets, every day.
Age Requirement: 65-plus

Smilie's Place (West End)
17202 – 95 Avenue; 443-3388
SAVE Seniors receive $1 off buffets all day Tuesday (lunch and dinner).
Age Requirement: 65-plus

CHINESE RESTAURANTS (DINE-IN) – SHERWOOD PARK

Smilie's Village Family Restaurant
981 Fir Street; 464-1200
SAVE Seniors' Night Tuesdays (excepting special occasions) – $9.95 for dinner buffet.
Age Requirement: 60-plus

CHINESE RESTAURANTS (DINE-IN) – ST. ALBERT

Beijing House Buffet
13619 St. Albert Trail; 482-6660
SAVE Senior pricing on lunch and dinner buffets.
Age Requirement: 65-plus

Golden Dynasty Restaurant
440 St. Albert Road; 418-2388
SAVE Seniors get $1 off at lunch and dinner buffets, always.
Age Requirement: 65-plus

Jade Village Restaurant
480, 140 St. Albert Road; 459-8899

SAVE Seniors pay $6.50 for the Monday to Friday lunch buffets (adult $7.25) and $9.85 for the Friday to Sunday dinner buffets (adult $10.95).
Age Requirement: 65-plus

Wonderland Restaurant and Chinese Cuisine & Buffet
141, 1 Hebert Road; 459-0066
SAVE Seniors receive $1 off evening buffets on Friday, Saturday and Sunday.
Age Requirement: 65-plus

CHINESE RESTAURANTS (DINE-IN) – STONY PLAIN

The Orient Family Restaurant
900, 4305 – Southpark Drive; 963-8277
SAVE Senior pricing on lunch buffets (Tuesday to Friday) and on dinner buffets (Thursday to Sunday).
INFORMATION This is an "MSG-free" restaurant.
Age Requirement: 65-plus

Chinese Restaurants – Take Out

Most, if not all, Chinese restaurants offer the take-out option so you can enjoy a take-out meal at home A discount on pick-up orders over a certain value is pretty standard. Some also offer free delivery within a specified delivery area. Both these options offer savings – one through a percentage off your bill and the other meaning you're saving gasoline and time. Check carefully when choosing which restaurant to order from, because restaurants deliver free within a restricted radius. Check the advertisements under the headings *"Chinese Foods"* and *"Restaurants."*

Department Store Restaurants

The Bay
In *The Bay* stores that have restaurants (and most of them do), they all offer the same senior discount – a 10 per cent discount, always. Below are the locations of *The Bay* restaurants in Edmonton:
• The Bay Market Square Grill at West Edmonton Mall; 444-1550

- The Bay Edmonton House Buffet at Southgate Mall; 435-9211
- The Bay Market Square Café at Londonderry Mall; 478-2931
- The Bay Café Expresso at Edmonton City Centre; 424-0151

SAVE Seniors receive a 10 per cent discount, always.

Age Requirement: 60-plus

Zellers

In the *Zellers* stores that have restaurants (and most of them do), they all offer the exact senior discount – a 10 per cent discount, always. Below are the locations of the *Zellers* restaurants in Edmonton:

- Meadowlark Shopping Centre; 484-1171
- Bonnie Doon Shopping Centre; 461-6776
- 3931 Calgary Trail; 436-2211
- Kingsway Garden Mall; 479-8414
- Mill Woods Town Centre; 468-7050
- Northgate Mall; 473-3828
- West Edmonton Mall; 444-1722

SAVE Seniors receive a 10 per cent discount, always.

Age Requirement: 55-plus

There is a restaurant in the Zellers in Sherwood Park at Sherwood Park Mall (467-7755) and a restaurant in the Zellers in St. Albert Centre (459-6641). The senior discount is offered at both.

Fine Dining

Also, see the section on Sunday Brunches as many fine dining establishments do offer senior discounts on their Sunday brunches.

FINE DINING – EDMONTON

David's Restaurant

8407 Argyll Road; 468-1167

SAVE 10 per cent senior discount on Monday evenings.

INFORMATION Some entrees can be ordered as half orders for the smaller appetite.

Age Requirement: 65-plus

The Mill Restaurant
8109 – 101 Street; 432-1838
SAVE A variety of senior selections are offered on the menu.
Age Requirement: 65-plus

Ric's Grill
www.ricsgrill.com
14229 – 23 Avenue; 497-7427
10190 – 104 Street; 429-4333
SAVE For those with smaller appetites, several specially-priced
Lighter Fare Entrees are offered.
Age Requirement: Anyone

FINE DINING – SHERWOOD PARK
Ric's Grill
340, 550 Baseline Road; 417-7427
See under Fine Restaurants – Edmonton.

FINE DINING – ST. ALBERT
Ric's Grill
24 Perron Street; 460-6602
See under Fine Restaurants – Edmonton.

International Cuisine
INTERNATIONAL CUISINE – EDMONTON
Bauernschmaus Restaurant (German)
6796 – 99 Street; 433-8272
SAVE Most entrees can be ordered as "senior portions."
Age Requirement: 65-plus

Oliveto Trattoria (Italian)
500 Riverbend Square; 435-6411
SAVE For smaller appetites, half-orders of menu items can be ordered.
Age Requirement: Anyone

Taurus Wok & Grill (*Thai cuisine*)
    29 Perron Street; 459-8677
SAVE Senior menu offered, always.
    Age Requirement: 65-plus

The Cajun House (*Cajun cuisine*)
    7 St. Anne Street; 460-8772
SAVE "Smaller portions" are featured on the menu.
    Age Requirement: Anyone

Fish 'N Chips & Seafood Restaurants

Joey's Only Seafood Restaurants
www.joeys-only.com
- 2609 – 66 Street; 485-1661
- 12222 – 137 Avenue; 473-5639
- 5004 – 98 Avenue; 461-7966
- 3040 Calgary Trail South; 440-3447
- 11308 – 104 Avenue; 421-1971
- 17018 – 95 Avenue; 483-1467
- 300 Manning Crossing; 413-8806
- Southgate Mall Food Court; 434-0691

PROMOTION Joey's Only Seafood Restaurants have a long-standing weekly special which is popular with many seniors. Each Tuesday, enjoy all you can eat fish and chips for just $7.99 per person (dine-in only) at most locations.

INFORMATION Their website advises customers of current and upcoming periodic promotions and contests.
    Age Requirement: Anyone

Pan's Fish & Chips
    6530 – 28 Avenue; 440-6696
SAVE Senior menu offered, always.
    Age Requirement: 65-plus

Joey's Only Seafood Restaurant
    270 Baseline Road; 467-8777

See under Fish & Chips and Seafood Restaurants – Edmonton.

Joey's Only Seafood Restaurant
3506 Tudorglen Market; 459-5089
See under Fish & Chips and Seafood Restaurants – Edmonton.

Joey's Only Seafood Restaurant
215 First Avenue; 962-1005
See under Fish & Chips and Seafood Restaurants – Edmonton.

Joey's Only Seafood Restaurant
6104 – 50 Street; 986-3474
See under Fish & Chips and Seafood Restaurants – Edmonton.

Hotel Restaurants

Burgundy Café at The Holiday Inn Southeast Edmonton
4520 – 76 Avenue; 468-5400
SAVE Seniors receive a 15 per cent discount, always.
Age Requirement: 60-plus

Cafe Lacombe at The Crowne Plaza Chateau Lacombe
www.chateaulacombe.com
10111 Bellamy Hill; 428-6611
SAVE Seniors save 10 per cent at the lunch buffet/salad bar, Monday to Friday.
Age Requirement: 65-plus

Continental Inn Dining Room
16625 Stony Plain Road; 484-7751
SAVE Lunch buffets Sunday to Friday – senior $9.70 (Adult $10.70) and dinner buffets every evening – senior $10.70 (Adult $12.25).

Age Requirement: 60-plus

Garden Terrace Restaurant at The Four Points Sheraton Hotel
7230 Argyll Road; 465-7931
SAVE Seniors receive a discount on dinner entrees after 5 p.m., always.
Age Requirement: 60-plus

Market Café at The Mayfield Inn
16615 – 109 Avenue; 930-4060
SAVE Monday to Friday lunch buffet is $10.95 for seniors ($12.95 adult).
Age Requirement: 55-plus

Pantry Restaurant at The Chateau Nova
www.novahotels.ca
159 Airport Road, adjacent to the City Centre Airport
SAVE Senior discount of 10 per cent, every day.
Age Requirement: 55-plus

Rutherford's at The Edmonton House Suite Hotel
10205 – 100 Avenue; 420-4359
SAVE Seniors receive a 15 per cent discount, always.
Age Requirement: 60-plus

HOTEL RESTAURANTS – SHERWOOD PARK

Albert's Homestead Grill in The Road King Inn
Yellowhead and Broadmoor Boulevard; 417-2921
SAVE Seniors menu offered always (coffee is free with orders from the senior menu). Evening buffet seven days a week with senior pricing.
Age Requirement: 55-plus

Franklin's Family Dining at Franklin's Inn
2016 Sherwood Drive; 467-1234
SAVE Seniors receive a 10 per cent discount on regular menu items every day (specials and buffets not included).
Age Requirement: 65-plus

HOTEL RESTAURANTS – ST. ALBERT

Michael's at the St.Albert Inn
156 St. Albert Road; 459-5551

SAVE Seniors receive a 10 per cent discount every day (regular menu – specials not included).
Age Requirement: 65-plus

HOTEL RESTAURANTS – LEDUC

O'Brians Fine Food at The Best Western Denham Inn
5207 – 50 Avenue; 986-2241

SAVE Seniors receive $1 off the luncheon buffets Monday to Friday and Sunday and receive $2 off the dinner buffets from Friday to Sunday.
Age Requirement: 55-plus

Luncheon Weekday Buffets (Fine Dining)

LUNCHEON WEEKDAY BUFFETS – EDMONTON

Sawmill Pacific Fish Company Restaurant
www.sawmillrestaurant.com
11560 – 104 Avenue; 429-2816

SAVE Seniors $9.95 Monday to Friday lunch buffet (Adult $12.95).

LOYALTY PROGRAM See under Sunday Brunches (Sawmill Restaurant Group) – Edmonton.
Age Requirement: 65-plus

Tom Goodchild's Moose Factory
4810 Calgary Trail South; 437-5616

SAVE Seniors $12.45 Monday to Friday lunch buffet (Adult $14.49)

LOYALTY PROGRAM See under Sunday Brunches (Sawmill Restaurant Group) – Edmonton.
Age Requirement: 65-plus

Pizza

There are a multitude of pizza establishments (several hundred) in Edmonton and area. Some offer dine-in and take-out while others offer take-out only.

Note that take-outs don't usually offer senior discounts but do offer extras like a free two-litre pop or a serving of wings with your order and many offer free delivery within a specific area (meaning you are saving gas and time). Also, some pizza establishments offer specials you should be aware of such as "buy one, get one free." Many of them distribute useful coupons in the mail or in coupon books.

Listed here are several pizza establishments. For smaller and mid-size ones, check directly with them and remember – ask if they have a senior discount or specials you can benefit from.

PIZZA – EDMONTON

Boston Pizza
- 7641 Argyll Road; 450-2900
- 3308 – 118 Avenue; 477-9101
- 4804 Calgary Trail South; 435-6001
- 5515 – 101 Avenue; 465-0771
- 12104 – 137 Avenue; 457-5777
- 10620 Jasper Avenue; 423-2333
- 5515 – 137 Avenue; 473-6370
- 10543 – 124 Street; 482-4471
- 11203 – 23 Avenue; 435-5005
- 5228 – 23 Avenue; 461-5400
- 180 Mayfield Common; 484-0042
- 10115 Princess Elizabeth Avenue; 477-9111
- 16521 – 97 Street; 456-5554
- 12711 – 97 Street; 476-8691
- 9804 – 22 Avenue; 463-9086
- 378 Bulyea Road; 431-8431
- 17002 – 90 Avenue; 481-6822
- West Edmonton Mall on Bourbon Street; 481-3400
- 12225 – 118 Avenue; 452-8585
- 10854 – 82 Avenue; 433-3151

SAVE You can obtain the Boston Pizza "You've Got Seniority" Coffee Card free – ask at any location for one. When you dine-in, show your card and receive one non-alcoholic beverage (hot or cold) free of charge (only one beverage per visit). The Boston Pizza menu has a selection of "half menu items" for smaller appetites.

LOYALTY REWARDS PROGRAM Boston Pizza is an Air Miles sponsor.

Age Requirement: 55-plus

Chicago Joe's
- 9604 – 111 Street; 479-4040
- 10425 – 158 Avenue; 457-3030

SAVE Senior menu offered, always.

Age Requirement: 65-plus

Pizza Hut
One telephone number for all: 310-1010
- 6504 – 28 Avenue
- 13324 – 50 Street
- 12410 – 137 Avenue
- 10011 – 178 Street
- 6923 – 172 Street
- 11515 – 104 Avenue
- 10809 – 82 Avenue
- 9718 – 153 Avenue
- 13133 – 82 Street
- 811 Saddleback Road
- 4004 – 50 Street
- 11740 – 34 Street
- 14715 – 40 Avenue
- 156 Street and 87 Avenue
- 9022 – 75 Street
- 13346 – 114 Avenue

SAVE Seniors receive a 10 per cent discount, every day, on both dine-in and take-out (but not on delivery orders).

Age Requirement: 65-plus

PIZZA – SHERWOOD PARK

Boston Pizza
- 11 Broadway Boulevard; 464-9999
- 967 Ordze Road; 467-2223

See under Pizza – Edmonton.

Pizza Hut
- 60, 993 Fir Street; 310-1010
- 10, 550 Baseline Road; 310-1010
See under Pizza - Edmonton.

PIZZA – ST. ALBERT

Boston Pizza
- 200 St. Albert Road; 458-8433
- 386 St. Albert Road; 458-5868
See under Pizza - Edmonton.

Pizza Hut
- 410 St. Albert Trail; 310-1010
- Village Landing Shopping Centre; 310-1010
- 230, 140 St. Albert Trail; 310-1010
See under Pizza - Edmonton.

PIZZA – SPRUCE GROVE

Boston Pizza
- 201 Calahoo Road; 962-0224
See under Pizza - Edmonton.

Pizza Hut
- 17 Westgrove Drive; 310-1010
See under Pizza - Edmonton.

PIZZA – STONY PLAIN

Boston Pizza
- 70 Boulder Boulevard; 963-5006
See under Pizza - Edmonton.

PIZZA – LEDUC

Boston Pizza
- 5309 – 50 Avenue; 986-6560
See under Pizza - Edmonton.

Pizza Hut
- 6205 – 50 Street; 310-1010
See under Pizza - Edmonton.

Steak & Pizza Restaurants

STEAK & PIZZA – EDMONTON

Black Bull Steak & Pizza
16642 – 109 Avenue; 489-3344
SAVE Senior menu offered, always.
Age Requirement: 65-plus

Dallas Pizza & Steak House
7834 – 106 Avenue; 466-1112
SAVE Senior menu offered, always.
Age Requirement: "Senior" (see page 3)

STEAK & PIZZA – SPRUCE GROVE

Peter's Pizza and Steaks
Co-Op Mall; 962-3023
SAVE Senior menu offered, always.
Age Requirement: 60-plus

STEAK & PIZZA – LEDUC

Kosmos Restaurant
5011 – 50 Avenue; 986-3122
SAVE Senior menu offered, always.
Age Requirement: 55-plus

Zambelli Prime Rib Steak & Pizza
6210 – 50 Street; 980-9669
SAVE A senior menu is offered always, plus smaller portions of
regular menu items for those with smaller appetites.
Age Requirement: "Senior" (see page 3)

Steak & Seafood Restaurants

STEAK & SEAFOOD – EDMONTON

Red Lobster
www.redlobster.ca
  • 4111 Calgary Trail South; 436-8510
  • 10111 – 171 Street; 484-0660
LOYALTY PROGRAM The Red Lobster Overboard Club is open to
everyone and is free to join (join on-line or at either of the
restaurants). By joining you will learn about special Red

Lobster events and discounts and will be automatically entered in a draw each month.
Age Requirement: Anyone

STEAK & SEAFOOD – ST. ALBERT

New York Steak and Seafood
81 Liberton Drive; 459-4808
SAVE For smaller appetites, half-orders from the menu are available.
Age Requirement: Anyone

Socrates Restaurant
208 St. Albert Road; 459-7880
SAVE A senior menu is offered always, plus senior menu items are two-for-one on Tuesday evenings.
Age Requirement: 55-plus

Sunday Brunches

What a nice outing on any Sunday. It's no secret that Sunday brunches are very popular. They usually run between 10 a.m. and 2 p.m. Reservations are required for most Sunday brunches, so to avoid disappointment be sure to telephone beforehand and enquire.

SUNDAY BRUNCHES – EDMONTON

Atrium Cafe at The Coast Terrace Inn
www.coastterraceinn.com
4440 – Gateway Boulevard; 437-6010
SAVE Senior $21.95 (Adult $23.95).
Age Requirement: 55-plus

Capital's Restaurant at The Sutton Place Hotel
www.edmonton.suttonplace.com
10235 – 101 Street; 428-7111
SAVE Senior $21.95 (Adult $23.95)
Age Requirement: 65-plus

Chateau Louis Hotel Dining Room
11727 Kingsway Avenue; 452-7770
SAVE Senior $16.95 (Adult $18.95)

Age Requirement: 65-plus

Continental Inn Dining Room
16625 Stony Plain Road; 484-7751
SAVE Senior $10.25 (Adult $11.25)
Age Requirement: 60-plus

Dalton's in The Greenwood Inn
4485 – Gateway Boulevard; 435-6796
SAVE Senior $18.95 (Adult $20.95).
Age Requirement: 65-plus

Empire Ballroom at The Fairmont Hotel Macdonald
www.fairmont.com
10065 – 100 Street; 424-5181
SAVE Senior $29.00 (Adult $34.00). Note that prices may vary on special occasions such as Mother's Day and holidays.
Age Requirement: 65-plus

Fantasy Grill Dining Room at The Fantasyland Hotel
West Edmonton Mall; 444-5538
SAVE Senior $17.95 (Adult $20.95)
Age Requirement: 60-plus

Grainfields Family Restaurant at The West Harvest Inn
17803 Stony Plain Road; 484-8000
SAVE Senior $12.95 (Adult $13.95)
Age Requirement: 65-plus

Julie's Bistro at The Edmonton Inn
www.edmontoninn.com
11830 Kingsway Avenue; 454-5454
SAVE Senior $17.50 (Adult $20.75).
Age Requirement: 65-plus

La Boheme Restaurant
6427 – 112 Avenue; 474-5693
SAVE Any senior ordering a half-portion of a hot brunch entree pays half-price (buffet also includes a selection of fruits and pastries).

Age Requirement: "Senior" (see page 3)

La Ronde at The Crowne Plaza Chateau Lacombe
www.chateaulacombe.com
   10111 Bellamy Hill; 428-6611
SAVE Senior $22.00 (Adult $26.00).
INFORMATION Guests can view the city's downtown and outlying areas from this unique revolving restaurant atop the Crowne Plaza Chateau Lacombe in the downtown core.
   Age Requirement: 65-plus

Mayfield Grill at The Mayfield Inn
www.mayfieldinnedmonton.com
   16615 – 109 Avenue; 930-4062
SAVE Senior $20.95 (Adult $23.95).
   Age Requirement: 60-plus

The Pantry Restaurant at The Chateau Nova
   159 Airport Road; 451-4700
SAVE Senior $9.95 (Adult $10.95)
   Age Requirement: 55-plus

Queen's Court Atrium at The Holiday Inn Palace
   4235 Gateway Boulevard; 438-1222
SAVE Senior $15.95 (Adult $17.95)
   Age Requirement: 65-plus

Sawmill Group of Restaurants
www.sawmillrestaurant.com
   There are four restaurants in the Sawmill Group of restaurants. See under Luncheon Weekday Buffets (Fine Dining) for details about luncheon buffets offered at several of their restaurants.

– The Sawmill Original Restaurant
   4725 Gateway Boulevard; 436-1950
SAVE Senior $16.95 (Adult $18.95)
   Age Requirement: 65-plus

– Sawmill Prime Rib & Steakhouse
    9504 – 170 Street; 486-5866
SAVE Senior $15.95 (Adult $17.95)
    Age Requirement: 65-plus

– Sawmill Pacific Fish Company Restaurant
    11560 – 104 Avenue; 429-2816
SAVE Senior $13.95 (Adult $17.95)
    Age Requirement: 65-plus

– Tom Goodchild's Moose Factory
    4810 Calgary Trail; 437-5616
SAVE Senior $19.95 (Adult $20.95)
    Age Requirement: 65-plus

LOYALTY PROGRAM It is free to join the Sawmill Loyalty Club,
    designed to show appreciation for repeat business at all four
    of the Sawmill Group of Restaurants. Once customers ac-
    cumulate 500 points, they are eligible for a $25 discount
    that will be applied to their next bill. As part of the Sawmill
    Birthday Club, customers who have purchased a minimum
    of four regular-priced entrees from the evening menu re-
    ceive up to $20.00 off a birthday dinner or lunch.

Steel's Café & Grill at The Executive Royal Inn West Edmonton
www.executivehotels.net
    10010 – 178 Street; 484-6000
SAVE Senior $14.95 (Adult $17.50)
    Age Requirement: 60-plus

Top of the Inn at The Delta Edmonton South
    4404 Gateway Boulevard; 431-3468
SAVE Senior $18.95 (Adult $22.95)
INFORMATION Enjoy a panoramic view of the city.
    Age Requirement: 65-plus

SUNDAY BRUNCHES – LEDUC

Gazebo Café at The Executive Royal Inn Leduc/Nisku
www.executivehotels.net

Across from the International Airport on Queen Elizabeth
II Highway; 986-1840
SAVE Senior $13.95 (Adult $16.95)
Age Requirement: 60-plus

Fast Food

Fast food outlets are found in many locations in Edmonton
and surrounding area. Many offer discounts to senior customers
You can choose among:
- Subs (submarine sandwiches)
- chicken
- pizza
- hamburgers
- tacos
- ice cream treats

Some fast-food establishments are part of corporately-
owned/operated chains (and thus offer savings in all of their
locations) while others are independently owned and operated
and offer savings specific to their location only. In many cases, if
the fast food outlet is in a food court of a shopping centre they do
not provide the senior discounts offered by stand-alone outlets.
The best bet? *Always ask if there is a senior discount.*

Arby's
Participating locations offer a 10 per cent discount (every day) to
seniors 65-plus.

A & W
At participating locations there are "Early Bird Senior Breakfast
Specials" (Monday to Wednesday before 11 a.m.) and "Senior
Dinner Specials" (Monday to Thursday from 4 to 6 p.m.) Age re-
quirement: "senior" (see page 3 for definition).

Dairy Queen
Participating locations offer a 10 per cent discount (every day) to
customers 65-plus.

Burger King
Participating locations offer a 10 per cent discount (every day) to
customers 65-plus.

Harvey's
Participating locations offer a "Senior Beverage" promotion
– a reduced rate on coffee, tea, hot chocolate and pop to any
"senior" (see page 3 for definition).

Kentucky Fried Chicken (KFC)
Participating locations offer a 10 per cent discount to seniors
60-plus on eat-in, drive-through and take-out (but not on delivery). A regular weekly promotion that is extremely popular is the
"Toonie Tuesday" promotion: an order of two pieces of chicken
and fries is $2.49 plus tax all day Tuesday.

McDonald's
Participating locations offer "Senior Coffee" every day at a reduced rate to any "senior"(see page XX for definition).

Mr. Sub
Participating locations offer the "VIP Club Card" (free) which
enables customers to collect stamps towards the purchase of a
free sub. The location where you collect the stamps is the location where you redeem the free sub.

Taco Bell
Participating locations offer a 10 per cent discount every day to
customers 65-plus.

Wendy's
Participating locations offer a 10 per cent discount every day to
customers 65-plus.
INFORMATION As part of its regular menu, Wendy's offers a
$1.39 Value Menu which has quite a number of choices.

Coffee Shops and Tea Houses

Aroma Café
139 Bonnie Doon Shopping Centre in Edmonton; 469-0101
CUSTOMER APPRECIATION PROGRAM They offer a stamp card
that allows customers who buy seven cups of gourmet coffee or tea to receive the eighth gourmet coffee or tea free;
program is free to join.

Age Requirement: Anyone

Brownstone's Coffee Café
Food Court, Capilano Mall (50 Street and 98 Avenue) in
Edmonton

CUSTOMER APPRECIATION PROGRAM Their stamp card provides
customers who buy 11 beverages with the 12th beverage
free; program is free to join.
Age Requirement: Anyone

Java Express
110, 4300 South Park Drive in Stony Plain; 968-1860

SAVE Senior customers save in two ways: they always receive a 10
per cent discount on coffee and desserts (dine-in), and they
also receive a 10 per cent discount on fresh-ground coffee
by the pound to take home and enjoy.
Age Requirement: 65-plus

JAX Bean Shop
12761 – 50 Street in Edmonton; 478-0480

SAVE There is a five per cent discount on coffee and desserts for
groups of five or more people, always.
Age Requirement: Anyone

Tim Hortons
Located in and around Edmonton, these Canadian coffee shops
are VERY popular. Look for the annual "Roll Up The Rim To Win
Contest" – you never know when you'll be a winner.

Timothy's World Coffee
EDMONTON/ST. ALBERT LOCATIONS
- Westmount Shopping Centre; 448-9900
- Edmonton City Centre; 420-6762
- 9777 – 102 Avenue; 424-2821
- West Edmonton Mall; 486-4262
- 178 Street/Callingwood Road; 489-0193
- 8137 – 104 Street; 433-8758
- and in St. Albert at 100, 21 Perron Street; 460-6875

SAVE Their free "Bean Cup Card" is available at all locations. For each half-pound of beans or ground coffee you buy to take home or give as a gift, you get a stamp on the card. When the stamp card is full, you are entitled to a free half-pound of the coffee of your choice.
Age Requirement: Anyone

Grocery Stores – Major

There are four large major grocery store chains in Edmonton and surounding communities: *Safeway, Save-On-Foods, Superstore* and *Sobey's/IGA Garden Market. Champion Family Foods* is an independent with one location on Jasper Avenue and 117 Street, downtown.

Each store chain provides consumers with weekly flyers so you can easily do some comparison shopping. Watch these weekly flyers carefully for coupons, "buy one, get one free" specials and the sale prices on particular products that week. Always use coupons if you have them.

Staff at *Safeway, Save-On Foods, Sobeys/IGA stores* and at *Champion Family Foods* are always happy to help senior customers reach items on upper shelves and pack their groceries at the till. But service doesn't end there – staff will take your grocery order to your car and load it into the trunk. Some (but not many) grocery stores offer parcel pick-up and you should make use of this service; it means you can go to your car, drive up to the store and staff will load your groceries. This is a great convenience in the cold winter months. Superstore has a little different retailing approach – you have to pack your own groceries and get them to your vehicle yourself. It also charges for plastic grocery bags to pack your purchases in but you can save money by taking along your own plastic grocery bags or re-usable cloth bags or even plastic bins. Superstore locations do have the added advantage of large book, toy, clothing, housewares and footwear departments, making them somewhat of a "one-stop shopping" option.

Most major grocery stores have in-store pharmacies so you can also drop off prescriptions and refill orders as you shop for your groceries.

The major grocery chains have good websites where you can access their weekly flyers electronically. There are links on all of their websites for free recipes and some have links for coupons. At the *Safeway* and *Save-On-Foods* websites, you can read about their respective customer appreciation programs.

The grocery stores provide handicapped parking stalls close to the entrance doors for those vehicles displaying placards.

Champion Family Foods

11720 Jasper Avenue; 451-9034

SAVE On Customer Appreciation Day, the first Tuesday of each month, customers receive five per cent off a minimum $25 grocery purchase (excepting postage stamps, lottery and tobacco).

INFORMATION Conveniently located on 117 Street and Jasper Avenue, with good bus service.

Age Requirement: Anyone

Safeway

www.safeway.com

In Edmonton there are 19 stores, and there are two stores in Sherwood Park, in St. Albert, one each in Spruce Grove, Stony Plain and Leduc.

SAVE Customers can apply for a Safeway Club Card to get instant savings each time they shop; grocery items vary week to week. The program is free to join. Savings are deducted automatically off the total bill at the checkouts (no coupons are required). By using the Safeway Club Card on the first Tuesday of each month and spending a minimum of $25, customers have their choice of 10 per cent off their total bill (some exceptions apply) or ten times the Air Miles points.

LOYALTY PROGRAM Safeway is an Air Miles sponsor.

Age Requirement: Anyone

Save-On Foods

www.saveonfoods.com

They have eight stores in Edmonton, two each in Sherwood Park and St. Albert.

SAVE Customers can apply for a Save-On-More Reward Card. Not only do club members earn points each time they shop, customers also save on specific grocery items which vary from week to week. By using the Save-On-More Card on the first Tuesday of each month and spending a minimum of $50, customers receive 15 per cent off their total bill (some exceptions apply).

LOYALTY PROGRAM Points earned with the Save-On-More Reward Card can be redeemed for products within the store, products from their catalogue or for air travel. Age Requirement: Anyone

Sobeys/IGA Garden Markets
www.sobeys.ca

Sobeys stores: 10 in Edmonton, one in Sherwood Park, one in St. Albert and one in Leduc. *IGA Garden Market* stores: 10 in Edmonton, one in Spruce Grove and one in Stony Plain.

SAVE On the first Tuesday of each month, when spending a minimum of $25, customers receive 10 per cent off their total bill (some exceptions apply). Age Requirement: Anyone

Superstore
www.superstore.ca

Five stores in Edmonton, one each in Sherwood Park, St. Albert and Spruce Grove.

SAVE With the coupon clipped from the Superstore flyer that comes out the first week of each month, customers spending a minimum of $250 receive $30 off their purchase (some exceptions apply). Age Requirement: Anyone

Specialty Food Stores

Many people choose to eat organically-grown produce, fruits, dairy and meat. Some customers like the idea of shopping at a smaller specialty grocery store that carries specialty produce, meats and products plus unique food items not available elsewhere.

The Big Fresh
10220 Jasper Avenue; 433-7374

SAVE 10 per cent discount on Wednesdays on supplements and body-care purchases.

LOYALTY PROGRAM This store has a "Preferred Customer Sign-Up Program" through which customers receive newsletters regarding promotions and specials. Anyone is welcome to sign up and the program is free to join.
Age Requirement: 65-plus for the discount

Buns and Roses Wholegrain Bakery Ltd.
6519 – 111 Street; 438-0098

SAVE Buy ten loaves of wholegrain bread and receive a 10 per cent discount, any day.
Age Requirement: Anyone

Sunterra Market
www.sunterramarket.com
- 5728 – 111 Street; 434-2610
- 201 Commerce Place (10150 Jasper Avenue); 426-3791

CUSTOMER APPRECIATION PROGRAM It is free to join the Fresh Rewards Program. Customers are given a keytag to present when they make purchases to gain reward points. The points can be redeemed for in-store bakery items, "grab and go" meals and Sunterra Gift Certificates. Members also receive *The Sunterra Times* newsletter by mail on a bimonthly basis; there are some great recipes featured each issue. Members also receive free treats on their birthday.
Age Requirement: Anyone

Nutter's Bulk and Natural Foods
4720 – 51 Avenue; 986-1257

SAVE 20 per cent discount on the first Tuesday of every month.
Age Requirement: Anyone

Prepared/Frozen Food Shops

M & M Meat Shops
www.mmmeatshops.com
- 238, 6655 – 178 Street; 481-8100
- 568 Riverbend Square; 437-3700
- 262 Meadowlark Shopping Centre; 489-6963
- 1000 Northgate Shopping Centre; 478-0515
- 340 Mill Woods Town Centre; 413-6900
- 109, 10939 – 23 Avenue; 415-5551
- 186 Bonnie Doon Shopping Centre; 414-6360
- 16528 – 95 Street; 475-5452
- 3812 – 137 Avenue; 473-4822
- 11544 – 104 Avenue; 429-4433

SAVE Seniors save five per cent on Senior's Day, which is every Tuesday.

CUSTOMER APPRECIATION PROGRAM The M & M Max Card is free to obtain. Just fill out a registration form at any of the shops. It entitles customers to flyer savings, money-saving offers and draws.

Age Requirement: 65-plus for the Senior's Day discount and anyone for the M & M Max Card

M & M Meat Shop
- 73, 993 Fir Street; 464-0201
- 160, 550 Baseline Road; 416-0482

See under Prepared/Frozen Food Stores – Edmonton.

Goodlife Foods
www.goodlife.ca
   380 St. Albert Road; 418-7864

CUSTOMER APPRECIATION PROGRAM It is free to join the Goodlife Rewards Program, which offers savings and discounts. Their computer tracks rewards for purchases.

INFORMATION Customers can also shop on-line. Ask about Goodlife Foods' free delivery policy. They have low-carb

and low-fat products and a good selection of "no sugar added" ice cream.
Age Requirement: Anyone

M & M Meat Shop
- 216, 2 Hebert Road; 460-8852
  See under Prepared/Frozen Food Stores – Edmonton.

PREPARED/FROZEN FOOD SHOPS – LEDUC

M & M Meat Shop
- 3, 5209 Discovery Way; 986-1049
  See under Prepared/Frozen Food Stores – Edmonton.

Warehouse and Discount Food Stores

There are several warehouse food stores in Edmonton. They look just like warehouses with high ceilings and concrete floors. There are no fancy displays nor is there staff available to carry your orders to your car. But there are real savings here via buying in bulk, by caselots or by warehouse packs. Remember, though, unless you can use all of a product before its expiry date (or life of the product) you're not saving money.

Costco
- 12450 – 149 Street; 454-1468
- 13650 – 50 Street; 475-8000
- 2616 – 91 Street; 577-1200

INFORMATION Membership open to anyone and cost per year is $50 (plus tax) for two cards. A new COSTCO is under construction in Sherwood Park.
Age Requirement: Anyone

The Grocery People Warehouse Market
14505 Yellowhead Trail; 451-0882

INFORMATION There is no membership cost and a card is not required to shop here; walk-in.
Age Requirement: Anyone

The Real Canadian Wholesale Club
- 14740 – 111 Avenue; 452-5411

- 6904 – 99 Street; 431-1090

INFORMATION No membership required; walk-in.
Age Requirement: Anyone

Valco Foods Discount Food Outlet
12222 – 137 Avenue; 457-7702
INFORMATION No membership required; walk-in.
Age Requirement: Anyone

Dessert Factory Outlets

There are several "direct-to-consumer" dessert outlets. They are:

Saxby Dessert Factory Outlet
4120 – 98 Street; 440-4179
Age Requirement: Anyone

WOW Factor Desserts Factory Retail Outlet
152 Cree Road in Sherwood Park; 464-0303
INFORMATION Closed Sundays and holidays.
Age Requirement: Anyone

Bakeries

BAKERIES – EDMONTON

B & A Bakery
12908 – 82 Street; 476-8585
SAVE 10 per cent senior discount on Tuesdays.
Age Requirement: 55-plus

Bon Ton Bakery
8720 – 149 Street; 489-7717
SAVE 10 per cent senior discount on Mondays.
Age Requirement: 55-plus

Cay's Bakery
15115 Stony Plain Road; 489-9740
SAVE 10 per cent senior discount on Tuesdays.
Age Requirement: 65-plus

Empress Bakery
     9932 – 82 Avenue; 433-8451
     SAVE 10 per cent senior discount on Wednesdays.
     Age Requirement: 65-plus

Discount Bakery Stores

     At the many *McGavin's Bread Basket Discount Bakery* outlets, you can get discounts on fresh bread and buns and even deeper discounts on day-old bread and buns. These outlets are "direct-to-consumer" and because a retailer is not involved in the selling equation, there are cost savings that McGavin is passing on to the customer. If you have a freezer, consider buying ten loaves at a time for great savings.

McGavin's Bread Basket Discount Bakery
SAVE Discounted bread and buns, always.
     Age Requirement: Anyone
ADDITIONAL SAVINGS Seniors can save even more money on
     "Senior Day" every Wednesday with a 10 per cent discount
     on purchases.
     Age Requirement: 60-plus

LOCATED IN EDMONTON
     • 9123 – 39 Avenue; 462-2180
     • 12620E – 132 Avenue; 452-5751
     • 12151 – 160 Street; 447-6595
     • 12751 – 50 Street; 457-1724

LOCATED IN SHERWOOD PARK
     • 19, 99 Wye Road; 449-1639

LOCATED IN ST. ALBERT
     • 3521 Tudor Glen; 460-0655

Ice Cream & Chocolates

     The "new kid on the block" for ice cream is *Marble Slab Creamery.* There are shops at South Edmonton Common (466-4741) and in Sherwood Park at #320 Baseline Village (416-9696). Both allow seniors 60-plus to order from the lower-priced children's selection of cones and cups. Ask for a stamp card for

"The Slab Club" and receive a stamp for every ice cream or yogurt cone purchased at either of these locations. A completed card entitles you to a free ice cream or yogurt cone. A third *Marble Slab Creamery* shop is located in the Old Strathcona area at 10358 – 82 Avenue (433-3636). Here, too, seniors 60-plus can order from the children's selection but their "Slab Card" promotion is exclusive to this location. Two more *Marble Slab Creamery* shops are slated to open in Edmonton in the near future.

At **Baskin Robbins Ice Cream** shops, offers vary. The Baskin Robbins at 10650 Whyte Avenue (431-1599) offers seniors 65-plus a 10 per cent discount every day. It's a great idea to stop in after shopping along Whyte Avenue in the Old Strathcona area, and save money on delicious ice cream. Other Baskin Robbins shops are located at various Edmonton shopping malls and some offer a stamp per purchase card as a promotion; be sure to ask them.

At **Laura Secord Chocolates** shops, offers also vary. At the Riverbend Square location (which is a Laura Secord/Hallmark Cards combination), seniors 65-plus can get 15 per cent off all regularly-priced items each and every Thursday. The discount covers both Laura Secord and Hallmark. The Southgate Shopping Centre Laura Secord offers seniors 65-plus a 10 per cent discount on regularly-priced items on the first Monday of each month.

Recipes, Nutritional Information and Meal Planning

See Chapter 13 (*The Internet*) for information about a myriad of free websites that have recipes you can print out and try. Many of these websites are sponsored by associations including the *Alberta Pork Producers* and *Alberta Barley Association*, as well as companies such as *Robin Hood Flour*.

Here are some sources for nutritional information and meal planning for seniors:

FREE *Alberta Department of Agriculture, Food and Rural Development* offers a toll-free line where you can get answers to questions about food safety and storage. The toll-free line is 1-800-892-8333.

FREE *The ATCO Blue Flame Kitchen*, 420-1010, is a great resource for Alberta seniors. You can talk to a professional home economist and ask questions about recipes, food, general nutrition and cooking. A major advantage is that because they are Alberta-based, the nutritionists are familiar with food products and brands available at grocery stores in Edmonton and area. *The ATCO Blue Flame Kitchen* also has a wonderful website: www.atcoblueflamekitchen.com.

FREE The following food companies have toll-free information lines; these lines are open Monday to Friday during business hours:

Bernardin Canning Help Line
1-888-430-4231

Certo Jams & Jellies
1-800-268-6038

Kraft Canada Consumer Centre
1-800-268-6450

Robin Hood Consumer Line (Smucker Foods of Canada)
1-800-268-3232

The Canadian Heart & Stroke Foundation
www.healthcheck.org

FREE Seeking nutritional information? This website offers valuable nutritional information and tips on shopping for healthy food choices.

Farmers' Markets

It's no secret that you can find good prices and value when purchasing fresh vegetables, fruits, herbs, eggs and meat products plus jams and jellies at farmers' markets. These markets generally operate from mid-May to late September each year.

There are a number of Alberta-approved farmers' markets in Edmonton and surrounding area. In Edmonton there are seven markets (including the Edmonton City Market downtown on 104th Street and the Old Strathcona Market). Sherwood Park has two farmers' markets, as does St. Albert, while the communities of Spruce Grove, Stony Plain and Leduc each have one.

Alberta Department of Agriculture, Food and Rural Development publishes its **Alberta Farmers' Markets** brochure each year. The free brochure is available at most visitor centres. For information on obtaining it, call 427-4514. They also provide a website with similar information: www.sunnygirl.ca. Also watch your newspaper for information on farmers' markets in your community

Liquor Stores

Liquor in moderation is the key. When entertaining, there's lots to choose from in the form of wines from a variety of countries, along with the standard beer and hard liquor offerings. Some people also like coolers or ice wines.

It is pretty standard that liquor stores and outlets offer some type of savings to senior customers, such as a percentage discount on purchases or days that are "GST-free."

You can also enquire at any liquor store about case discounts, as there may be savings in that area.

Here are some of the larger chain liquor stores, including their addresses, discount given and age requirement to get the discount. Several of the larger independent liquor stores have also been included. Keep in mind that many of the small neighbourhood independents also offer some type of discount – *be sure to ask.*

Jasper Place Liquor Store
15312 Stony Plain Road in Edmonton; 481-2642
SAVE Five per cent senior discount on Tuesdays.
Age Requirement: 65-plus

Liquor Barn
SAVE All Liquor Barn outlets have a "Seniors Day Tuesday."
INFORMATION Discounts themselves and age requirements differ from outlet to outlet.

LOCATED IN EDMONTON
- 8940 – 82 Avenue (Five per cent; 65-plus)
- 11035 – 23 Avenue (Five per cent; 60-plus)

- 14005 Victoria Trail (Five per cent; 55-plus)
- 15277 Castledowns Road (Five per cent; 65-plus)
- 3927 – 34 Street (Five per cent; 60-plus)
- 9772 – 182 Street (Five per cent; 60-plus)
- 4353 – 50 Street (Five per cent on beer and 10 per cent on hard liquor; 55-plus)
- 14010 – 66 Street (Five per cent; 60-plus)

LOCATED IN SHERWOOD PARK

- 30E, 2020 Sherwood Drive (Five per cent; 55-plus)

Liquor Depot

SAVE Most locations offer a discount of some type to seniors. Those that do are listed below.

INFORMATION Discounts themselves and age requirements differ from outlet to outlet.

LOCATED IN EDMONTON

- Mayfield Common (Seven per cent, every day, 65-plus)
- Bonnie Doon Mall (Four per cent, Mondays, 65-plus)
- Meadowlark Shopping Centre (Five per cent, Mondays, 65-plus)
- 15317 – 97 Street (Five per cent, Mondays, 65-plus)
- 16562 – 95 Street (Five per cent, Mondays, 55-plus)
- 10164 – 109 Street (Five per cent, Mondays, 65-plus)
- 6120 Terrace Road (Five per cent, Mondays, 65-plus)
- 6538 – 28 Avenue (Five per cent, Mondays, 65-plus)
- 252 Manning Crossing (Five per cent, Mondays, 65-plus)
- 11730 Jasper Avenue (Five per cent, every day, 60-plus)
- Westmount Shopping Centre (Five per cent, every day, 65-plus)
- 5004 – 98 Avenue (Seven per cent, Mondays, 55-plus)
- 8169 – 99 Street (Five per cent, Tuesdays, 65-plus)

LOCATED IN SHERWOOD PARK

- 993 Fir Street (Five per cent, Mondays, 60-plus)

Liquor World

SAVE Most locations offer a discount of some type to seniors. Those that do are listed.

INFORMATION Discounts themselves and age requirements differ from outlet to outlet.

LOCATED IN EDMONTON

- 13620 – 93 Street (Five per cent, Tuesdays, 65-plus)
- 4223 – 23 Avenue (Six per cent, Tuesdays, 55-plus)
- 12902 – 82 Street (Five per cent, Tuesdays, 60-plus)
- 11724 – 104 Avenue (Five per cent, Tuesdays, 55-plus)
- 13320 – 114 Avenue (Five per cent, every day, 65-plus)
- 11011 – 51 Avenue (Five per cent, Tuesdays, 65-plus)

LOCATED IN SHERWOOD PARK

- 1020 Sherwood Drive (Five per cent, Mondays, 60-plus)

LOCATED IN ST. ALBERT

- 100, 2 Hebert Road (Five per cent, Mondays, 65-plus)
- 7 Inglewood Drive (Five per cent, Tuesdays, 60-plus)

156 St. Liquor Store

10149 – 156 Street in Edmonton; 484-6937

SAVE Five per cent senior discount on Mondays, Wednesdays and Fridays.
Age Requirement: 65-plus

Preferred Alberta Liquor Stores

SAVE Most locations offer a discount of some type to seniors. Those that do are listed.

INFORMATION Discounts themselves and age requirements differ from outlet to outlet.

LOYALTY PROGRAM All Preferred Liquor Store outlets are Air Mile sponsors; minimum $20 purchase required to earn Air Miles.

LOCATED IN EDMONTON

- Beverly Crest Liquor Mart (Six per cent, Tuesdays – "Customer Appreciation Day", anyone)
- Grapes & Grain Liquor Store; 95 Avenue and 170 Street (Seven per cent, every day, 65-plus)
- Liquor International; 15102 Stony Plain Road (Five per cent, every day, 65-plus)
- Ottewell Liquor Mart (Five per cent, Mondays, 60-plus)

- Rosslyn Hotel Liquor Store (Five per cent, every day, 55-plus)

LOCATED IN ST. ALBERT

- Campbell Liquor Store; 3 Curial Drive (Five per cent, Wednesdays, 65-plus)
- St. Albert Inn Liquor Store, 156 St. Albert Road (Five per cent, Mondays, 60-plus)

LOCATED IN SPRUCE GROVE

- Grove Liquor Shoppe; 106, 636 King Street (Five per cent, Mondays, 65-plus)

LOCATED IN LEDUC

- Corinthia Liquor; 6, 4302 – 50 Street (Five per cent, every day, 65-plus)

Safeway Wine and Spirits
- 6106A – 50 Street in Leduc; 986-0050

SAVE Five per cent senior discount every Monday.

LOYALTY REWARDS PROGRAM *Safeway Wine and Spirits* is an Air Miles sponsor; minimum $20 purchase to earn Air Miles.
Age Requirement: 65-plus

Sherbrooke Liquor
- 11819 St. Albert Trail in Edmonton; 455-4556

SAVE Five per cent senior discount, every day.
Age Requirement: 65-plus

Sobey's Western Cellars
SAVE "Customer Appreciation No-GST Tuesday" on the first Tuesday of every month; save seven per cent on all purchases at all locations.
Age Requirement: Anyone

LOCATED IN EDMONTON

- 15353 Castle Downs Road
- 14272 – 23 Avenue
- 5221 – 23 Avenue
- 4903 – 184 Street

LOCATED IN SHERWOOD PARK
- 120 Lakeland Ridge Shopping Centre
- 688 Wye Road

LOCATED IN SPRUCE GROVE
- 168 Highway 16 West

LOCATED IN LEDUC
- 5425 – 50 Street

Spirits

SAVE Most locations offer a senior discount of some type to seniors. Those that do are listed below.

INFORMATION Discounts themselves and age requirements differ from outlet to outlet. Each location listed offers their particular senior discount every day.

LOCATED IN EDMONTON
- 7482 – 106 Avenue (Three per cent, 55-plus)
- 11708 – 34 Street (Three per cent, 55-plus)
- 11354 – 104 Avenue (Three per cent, 60-plus)
- 1503 – 50 Street (Three per cent, 55-plus)
- 11314 Jasper Avenue (Seven per cent, 65-plus)

LOCATED IN SHERWOOD PARK
- 590 Baseline Road (Three per cent, 65-plus)
- 101 Granada Boulevard (Five per cent, 65-plus)
- 665 Baseline Road (Three per cent, 55-plus)
- 260, 664 Wye Road (Three per cent, 55-plus)

LOCATED IN ST. ALBERT
- Mission Hill Plaza (Five per cent, 55-plus)
- 114, 22 Sir Winston Churchill Avenue (Three per cent, 55-plus)

LOCATED IN SPRUCE GROVE
- 250 King Street (10 per cent, 55-plus)
- 70 McLeod Avenue (Three per cent, 55-plus)

Chapter 2

Entertainment

Do you enjoy attending concerts or dinner theatres? Is attending a sports game your interest? Or perhaps you like playing bingo. Well, if you've ever wondered whether there are good senior discounts on entertainment activities, there are!

This chapter is chock-full of entertainment options available in Edmonton and surrounding communities.

Tickets for Events: Box Offices

Most arts and theatre groups have their own box offices, selling tickets exclusively for their own productions or concerts (for example, the Citadel Theatre Box Office sells only tickets for Citadel Theatre productions and the Winspear Box Office sells only tickets for Winspear Centre events).

Some of the smaller theatre and musical groups don't have their own box office, but choose to engage the services of a box office such as TicketMaster or TIX-On-The-Square. When a headline entertainer, touring musical or major event comes to Edmonton (at venues including the Northern Alberta Jubilee Auditorium, Rexall Place, and Shaw Conference Centre), you would contact the following box offices to obtain tickets. *Remember to ask if there is a senior ticket category and price... because often there is!*

TicketMaster – *call 451-8000*

INFORMATION You can also go directly to a TicketMaster outlet to purchase tickets in person. They are located in many shopping malls and at venues such as the Northern Alberta Jubilee Auditorium, and Festival Place in Sherwood Park.

TIX-On-The-Square – *call 420-1757*

INFORMATION You can also go directly to the TIX-On-The-Square outlet in Churchill Square to purchase tickets in person.

Concerts – Live Music!

For concerts by headline performing artists who come to Rexall Place, Northern Alberta Jubilee Auditorium or Winspear Centre, there is sometimes senior pricing on tickets. Be sure to ask about senior pricing when you call or stop in to purchase tickets.

Alberta Baroque Ensemble
www.albertabaroque.com

INFORMATION Performances at Robertson-Wesley United Church (October to April season). Tickets: 467-6531 or at the door.

SAVE Senior pricing on both season tickets and on single tickets; single ticket senior $17 (Adult $22).
Age Requirement: "Senior" (see page 3).

Edmonton Chamber Music Society

INFORMATION Performances at Convocation Hall at the University of Alberta (September to May season). Tickets: TIX-On-The Square (420-1757).

SAVE If you choose to purchase a season's ticket subscription, there is senior pricing.
Age Requirement: Anyone

Edmonton Classical Guitar Society

INFORMATION Performances at Muttart Hall in Alberta College (October to May season). Tickets: TIX-On-The-Square (420-1757).

SAVE Senior patrons save on both season subscriptions and single
tickets.
Age Requirement: 60-plus

Edmonton Jazz Society
www.yardbirdsuite.com
11 Tommy Banks Way; Tickets: 432-0248
INFORMATION Concerts showcasing local, national and interna-
tional jazz performers. Season is September to June.
SAVE Senior pricing on annual subscriptions and also $4 off each
Yardbird Suite show advertised in the society newsletter.
Age Requirement: "Senior" (see page 3).

Edmonton Opera
www.edmontonopera.com
Performances at the Northern Alberta Jubilee Auditorium.
Season: November to March. Tickets: Edmonton Opera Box
Office (429-1000) or TicketMaster (451-800).
SAVE Senior prices are offered on subscriptions only (not single
tickets) for Tuesday and Thursday performances in four
of the seven seating categories (main, orchestra main and
first balcony dress excluded) with prices ranging between
$57.30 and $150.30, depending on seat placement (comparable prices for adults: between $63.30 to $168.30).
Note that there is no senior pricing offered at the Saturday
performances on a subscription basis. Anyone can benefit
from the discounts on tickets purchased for a group of 10
or more.
Age Requirement: 65-plus for senior pricing

Edmonton Symphony Orchestra
www.edmontonsymphony.com
INFORMATION Performances at Hawrelak Park for "Symphony
Under the Sky" and at the Winspear Centre For Music
downtown for their September to May season. Tickets:
Winspear Box Office (428-1414).
SAVE For season tickets, there is senior pricing offered on most of
the series. The only senior discount on single tickets is for
the annual Handel's Messiah, with senior tickets ranging

from $25-$65 (Adult tickets ranging from $30 to $70). The "Rush Program" is also available to senior patrons. Rush tickets to all ESO performances are $15 (limit of two per person); the tickets go on sale two hours prior to each concert and are subject to availability. Valid ID is required to purchase these tickets.
Age Requirement: 65-plus

Music Wednesdays At Noon Series
INFORMATION Performances by local musicians playing instruments ranging from the bass trombone to the oboe. The venue is the McDougall United Church downtown in the lower level banquet hall (101 Street, one block south of Jasper Avenue). Concerts are held every Wednesday from 12:10 to 12:50 p.m. during October and November, and between January and May. You are encouraged to bring your bag lunch to eat as you listen.
FREE Admission is free (however, donations are most welcome).
Age Requirement: Anyone

World at the Winspear Concert Series
INFORMATION Performances at the Winspear Centre for Music (October to May season). Tickets: Winspear Box Office (428-1414).
SAVE Although there are no specific senior discounts any patron who purchases tickets for between four and seven concerts receives a 10 per cent discount on the single ticket prices. If a patron buys tickets to all eight concerts in the series, the savings are 18 per cent off regular prices.
Age Requirement: Anyone

Other Groups
SAVE The following groups offer senior pricing to their concerts:
  • Edmonton Youth Orchestra
  • Department of Music, University of Alberta
  • Pro Coro Canada
  • The Richard Eaton Singers
  • Edmonton Chamber Music Society

Dance

Alberta Ballet

www.albertaballet.com

INFORMATION Performances at the Northern Alberta Jubilee
   Auditorium; Tickets: TicketMaster (451-8000). Season is
   October to May.

SAVE Season subscriptions have senior pricing for tickets in the
   gold, silver and bronze seating categories and the same
   pricing is offered on single ticket purchases (there is no
   senior pricing offered in the diamond or platinum categories). Also, "rush tickets" are available (at discounted
   prices) to senior patrons the day of any performance (call
   TicketMaster prior to 3 p.m.).
   Age Requirement: 65-plus

Three other dance groups that offer senior pricing to their
performances are:
- Brian Webb Dance Company
- Cheremosh Ukrainian Dance Company
- Citie Ballet

Live Theatre

If you are a fan of live theatre then you are fortunate.
Edmonton boasts a wide array of productions and there is great
senior pricing to be found. Here's a bit of trivia – Edmonton has
more live theatre groups per capita than any other Canadian city!

Citadel Theatre

www.citadeltheatre.com

   9828 – 101 A. Avenue; Box Office: 425-1820

SAVE Senior ticket pricing offered on most categories of subscription packages and single tickets. The Citadel Theatre
   also offers "rush tickets" (one hour before theatre performances, tickets go on sale for 50 per cent off). "Pay what
   you can tickets" are also available for one performance of
   each play in the Mainstage and Rice Theatre Series. A block
   of tickets is reserved and goes on sale one hour before cur-

tain; there are suggested minimums and the box office can explain these to you.

INFORMATION If you are a season ticket patron, enquire about the Citadel Theatre's 3M Senior Club. Note that the theatre is accessible for wheelchair patrons and infrared headsets are available for patrons with hearing loss.

Age Requirement: 65-plus for senior tickets pricing; Anyone for "rush tickets" and "pay what you can tickets".

Shadow Theatre
www.shadowtheatre.org

INFORMATION Performances at the Varscona Theatre in Old Strathcona; Box Office: 434-5564

SAVE Senior patrons receive a discount on annual subscriptions (Premium Pass). Single tickets (excepting previews) are also discounted for senior patrons. Anyone can save by attending Saturday afternoon "Pay What You Can" performances. Tuesday evening performances during the play's run are "two admissions for the price of one."

Age requirement: 65-plus for senior pricing

Theatre Network
www.attheroxy.com

INFORMATION Performances at the ROXY Theatre (124 Street and 107 Avenue). Season runs September to March. Tickets: Theatre Network Box Office: 453-2440.

SAVE The "Annual Subscription Flex Pass" has a senior pricing category of $68 (Adult $85) and offers unlimited flexibility and exchange privileges. Another saving option is the "preview shows" annual subscription category (held a Tuesday or Wednesday before a play officially opens), with savings of 65 per cent off regular ticket prices.

Age Requirement: "Senior" (see page 3) for the Flex Pass; Anyone for the preview shows.

Other Groups
SAVE Some other live theatre groups that offer senior pricing to their performances are:
- Northern Light Theatre

- Studio Theatre
- Walterdale Playhouse

Dinner Theatre

Jubilations Dinner Theatre
www.jubilations.ca
> West Edmonton Mall; Box Office: 484-2424
> Season: year-round

SAVE "Senior Special" on Wednesday evenings with tickets $33.95 (Adult $48.95); the show running over the Christmas/New Year period is not included in the "Senior Special."

INFORMATION Enquire about the theatre's "Birthday Discount" if you are celebrating a birthday the day you are planning to attend.
> Age Requirement: 55-plus for "Senior Special"; Anyone for "Birthday Discount."

Mayfield Dinner Theatre
www.mayfieldinnedmonton.com
> 16615 – 109 Avenue; Box Office: 483-4051
> Season: year-round

SAVE There are no specific senior discount, but by attending the Wednesday Brunch or Tuesday evening performances, you'll pay less for tickets. Costs per person for these two categories range from $37 to $49, depending on seating (a Saturday evening show costs between $62 and $72, depending on seating).
> Age Requirement: Anyone

Performing Arts Venues in Surrounding Communities

The following performing arts centre venues usually run their seasons between September and May. Their seasons are made up of musical concerts, theatre productions and performances by headline entertainers such as musicians and comedians.

The Arden Theatre in St. Albert
www.ardentheatre.com
    5 St. Anne Street; Box Office: 459-1542
SAVE Senior pricing is offered on some of the shows during the
    season; enquire at the box office about specific shows or
    refer to the season brochure. The Arden Theatre's "Buy &
    Save Program" is a way to save on regular tickets through-
    out the season. You will receive 10 per cent discount if you
    purchase tickets for three to six shows; 15 per cent discount
    for seven to 11 shows; and 25 per cent discount for 12 or
    more shows.
    Age Requirement: 65-plus for single tickets when offered on
    particular shows; Anyone for the "Buy & Save Program."

Festival Place in Sherwood Park
    100 Festival Way; Box Office: 449-3378
SAVE The "Special Offer for Patrons" program allows you to save
    $5 off each ticket when you pre-purchase five or more regu-
    lar season performances (these must be separate perfor-
    mances and some exceptions do apply).
FREE Enquire about the "Festival Place Free Movie Nights" held
    on selected Sunday evenings and featuring classic movies
    which have included *My Fair Lady* and *The Last Waltz*.
    Age Requirement: Anyone

Horizon Stage Performing Arts Centre in Spruce Grove
www.horizonstage.com
    1001 Calahoo Road; Box Office: 962-8995
SAVE Senior pricing is offered on most shows during the season;
    phone the box office about specific shows or refer to the
    season brochure. The "Create Your Own Subscription Ticket
    Promotion" (available only until the third week of October
    each year) is a way to save on regular tickets throughout
    the season. If you purchase tickets to two or three shows,
    you receive a 10 per cent discount and four or five shows
    earns a 15 per cent discount while six-plus shows earns a
    20 per cent discount (some exceptions as to shows included
    in offer). Group discounts are also available.

Age Requirement: 65-plus to obtain senior pricing for single tickets when offered on particular shows; Anyone for the "Create Your Own Subscription Ticket Promotion."

Movies

It's always fun to see a movie on the big screen, and there are good discounts for seniors.

Most movie theatres in Edmonton and surrounding communities showcase the new release movies. The senior admission prices are equal to or better than matinee prices and the "Tuesday specials," so always ask for the senior admission rate. *In fact, at some movie theatres, the senior admission is almost half price of the adult admission charged.*

Also, there are several discount theatres that showcase movies several months after they have been released. So, if you can wait a few months to see a particular movie, you'll save money by patronizing these establishments.

Cineplex/Famous Players/Galaxy Theatres
www.cineplex.com and www.famousplayers.com

INFORMATION On these websites you can see a summary of movies being shown and view trailers. You can also purchase tickets on-line if you wish.

LOCATED IN EDMONTON

- Cineplex Odeon at 14231 - 137 Avenue; 732-2236
SAVE Senior $8 (Adult $13.95)
Age Requirement: 65-plus

- Cineplex Odeon at 1525 - 99 Street; 436-8585
SAVE Senior $8 (Adult $13.95)
Age Requirement: 65-plus

- Silver City West Edmonton Mall; 444-2400
SAVE Senior $8 (Adult $10.95)
Age Requirement: 65-plus

INFORMATION IMAX presentations at Silver City West Edmonton Mall appear under "IMAX Movies" elsewhere in this chapter.

LOCATED IN SHERWOOD PARK

– Galaxy Theatre at Sherwood Park Mall; 416-0150
SAVE Senior $6.75 (Adult $11.75)
        Age Requirement: 65-plus

Empire Theatres
www.empiretheatres.com
INFORMATION On the website, you can view trailers of current
        movies.

THEATRES – EDMONTON

– Westmount Centre Cinemas; 455-8726
SAVE Senior $5.75 (Adult $8.95)
        4211 – 139 Avenue; 472-7600
SAVE Senior $6 (Adult $11)
        City Centre at 10200 – 102 Avenue; 421-7020
SAVE Senior $6 (Adult $11)
        Age Requirement: 65-plus

– Gateway 8 Cinemas
        2950 Calgary Trail South; 436-6977
SAVE Senior $6.25 (Adult $8.95)
        Age Requirement: 65-plus

Other Theatres
THEATRES – SPRUCE GROVE

– Magic Lantern Theatre
        205 Main Street in Spruce Grove; 962-2332
SAVE Senior $5 (Adult $8)
        Age Requirement: 65-plus

THEATRE – LEDUC

– Leduc Cinemas
        4702 – 50 Street; 986-2728
SAVE Tuesday, Saturday, Sunday and holiday matinees are $5 ad-
        mission.
        Age Requirement: Anyone

Discount Movie Theatres

INFORMATION At discount movie theatres, which show movies that have been out for a few months, the admission price is the same for everyone, but you'll find good value here.

LOCATED IN EDMONTON

– *Cinema City 12 at 3633 – 99 Street*; 463-5481
SAVE Admission $2.25 all day Tuesdays and before 6 p.m. on other days; $3.50 after 6 p.m. all days, and $3.50 for "Midnight Movies" on Fridays and Saturdays.
Age Requirement: Anyone

– *Cineplex Odeon West Mall 8 Theatre*; 444-1829
SAVE All seats $3.50 for all showtimes.
Age Requirement: Anyone

– *Movies 12 at 5074 – 130 Avenue*; 472-9779
SAVE Admission $2.25 all day Tuesdays and before 6 p.m. on other days; $3.50 after 6 p.m. all days, and $3.50 for "Midnight Movies" on Fridays and Saturdays.
Age Requirement: Anyone

IMAX Movies

LOCATED IN EDMONTON

– *IMAX at the Telus World of Science (formerly Odyssium)*
11211 – 142 Street; 451-3344
SAVE Senior $8.95 (Adult $9.95)
INFORMATION Info on selected IMAX films, technology for the hearing and visually impaired is available. The theatre is fully wheelchair accessible.

– *Silver City Movie Theatre (IMAX)*
West Edmonton Mall; 444-2400
SAVE Senior $10.50 (Adult $13.45)
Age Requirement: 65-plus

Edmonton Film Society

INFORMATION Seniors residing in the Edmonton area are fortunate to have the opportunity to see films from yesteryear as part of an ongoing film series presented by the Edmonton

Film Society. This is a non-profit group and movies are screened at the Royal Alberta Museum Theatre. Further information can be obtained at the Museum website: www.royalalbertamuseum.ca.

SAVE Senior admission $4 (Adult $5)
Age Requirement: 65-plus

FREE The *Golden Memories Film Club* shows free classic movies once per month at Trinity Lutheran House. Information: 989-3166.

Annual Events

Annual events are eagerly awaited as the calendar turns! Some are free to attend while others offer discount pricing for seniors. Watch your local newspaper for specifics of these events.

Canada Day Festivities

When: July 1st; events shown below are free to attend:
- Events at the Alberta Legislature;
- Silly Summer Parade on Whyte Avenue; and
- Fireworks in the evening, downtown.

Ice On Whyte

When: Mid-January to Mid-February and free to attend.

INFORMATION Watch ice sculptures being designed and built over the four-week festival. You'll want to attend at least once at the beginning to watch these ice sculptures being created and then again near the end to see the finished ice sculptures. The festival is held in McIntyre Park in the Old Strathcona area and is sponsored by the Old Strathcona Business Association.

Klondike Days

www.klondikedays.com
Phone 423-2822
When: Mid- to late July annually

INFORMATION This is a 10-day event with a midway at Edmonton Northlands plus downtown activities and events.

FREE Many events during Klondike Days are free: the Klondike Days Parade, Sunday Afternoon Promenade, noon-hour activities downtown plus many pancake breakfasts around Edmonton.

SAVE Seniors' Day at the Exhibition (Edmonton Northlands) is on the Wednesday of the event with senior admission $3 (Adult $8). Seniors' Day has been sponsored in part by the *Edmonton Senior* newspaper annually for quite a few years. Age Requirement: 60-plus for Seniors' Day at the Exhibition

St. Albert Rainmaker Rodeo
1-888-459-1725
When: Annually in late May.

INFORMATION This is a three-day event featuring a parade, rodeo and midway.

SAVE "Seniors' Night" is the Friday night of the event. Those of senior age get free admission to the rodeo and exhibition grounds. Admission to the exhibition grounds is discounted on the Saturday and Sunday of the event to those of senior age at $7 (Adult $10). Note that midway rides are charged separately and you need to purchase tickets to ride. Age Requirement: "Senior" (see page 3)

Other events
INFORMATION Three great annual parades (and they are free to watch) and some great New Year's Eve fireworks (also free to watch) are:
- Cariwest Caribbean Festival Parade (early August)
- Leduc Santa Claus Parade (late November; sponsored by the Leduc & District Chamber of Commerce)
- Edmonton Indoor Santa Claus Parade & Light-Up Downtown (early December; sponsored by the Edmonton Downtown Business Association)
- New Year's Eve (free fireworks in downtown Edmonton)

Festivals
Edmonton and outlying communities are well known as hosts for many exciting festivals. And the good news for seniors?

Some of these festivals are free to attend and others have good senior pricing options.

Blueberry Bluegrass Festival

www.blueberrybluegrass.com
>   Telephone: 1-888-526-6464

INFORMATION This three-day festival of bluegrass music is held annually in July at Exhibition Park in Stony Plain.

FREE Seniors attend this festival free of charge.
>   Age Requirement: 65-plus

Edmonton Folk Music Festival

www.efmf.ab.ca
>   Telephone: 429-1899

INFORMATION A three-day festival annually held in August in the Edmonton's Gallagher Park in the river valley. There is no parking on-site so Park 'n Ride travels in from the Bonnie Doon Shopping Centre (seniors 65-plus ride for free). Wheelchair access on-site is available and volunteers can assist your ability to move around the site; a special seating area at mainstage is available. People planning to attend the festival who have a hearing impairment should enquire about the installed magnetic induction loops. Braille and large-print festival information is at the Information Tent for those with a visual impairment.

FREE Seniors attend free of charge; you may be asked for ID at the gate. Adults attending the Edmonton Folk Music Festival pay between $109 and $150 for a four-day pass depending on the purchase date of the pass.
>   Age Requirement: 65-plus

Edmonton Heritage Festival

>   Telephone: 488-3378

www.heritage-festival.com

INFORMATION A three-day festival celebrating Edmonton and area's cultural diversity that is held annually in early August at Hawrelak Park.

FREE The festival is free to attend and you'll enjoy multicultural dancing, music and theatre. There is a charge for food tick-

ets (everyone pays the same price) should you wish to take in this aspect of the festival. Donations are gratefully accepted to the Edmonton Food Bank. As there is no parking on site, bus service brings you into the park. Seniors 65-plus can save on "Park and Ride" on Edmonton Transit with a ticket that costs $1.75 per person (Adult $2).
Age Requirement: Anyone and 65-plus for "Park and Ride"

Edmonton Street Performer's Festival
Telephone: 425-5162
www.edmontonstreetfest.com
INFORMATION A 10-day festival held in downtown Edmonton in July that showcases performers such as comedians, jugglers and unicyclists in outdoor shows in and around Churchill Square. A great festival to take your grandchildren or great-grandchildren to! Note that Churchill Square is wheelchair accessible.
FREE All outdoor performances are free to watch and enjoy but tossing in some cash when they pass around the hat is encouraged!
Age Requirement: Anyone

Festival of Trees
www.festivaloftrees.ab.ca
Telephone: 407-2786
INFORMATION A four-day Christmas festival held annually in support of the University of Alberta Hospitals at the Shaw Conference Centre. Showcased are decorated Christmas trees and wreaths and there is on-going musical entertainment on the performance stage.
SAVE Senior admission $3 (Adult admission $6)
Age Requirement: 60-plus

The Fringe in Old Strathcona
www.fringetheatreadventures.ca
Telephone: 448-9000
INFORMATION The Fringe is a ten-day festival of theatre performances held each August and is the second-largest theatre festival in the world!

SAVE Although there are no particular senior discounts, you can save by purchasing a "Frequent Fringe Pass." Purchase of this pass gives you admission into any ten performances at The Fringe (saving you 25 per cent off regular ticket prices).

FREE During The Fringe, the Old Strathcona area hosts many activities and performers.
Age Requirement: Anyone

The Works Arts & Design Festival
www.theworks.ab.ca
426-2122

FREE Held in Edmonton annually in late June and early July, this 13-day festival features art and design exhibits and cultural entertainment in venues around the downtown core (Sir Winston Churchill Square and various office buildings and art galleries).
Age Requirement: Anyone

Hot Air Balloon Rides... Up, Up and Away!

Windship Aviation
438-0111
www.windshipaviation.com

Windship Aviation in Edmonton offers a great deal for seniors! If you've always wanted to go on a hot air balloon ride, here's your chance!

SAVE The seniors' rate is $199 person (Adult $229). You can also save if you choose a weekday morning flight (excluding holidays) as all flights are $169.00 per person for anyone.

INFORMATION Flights take place year-round except January, February and the first two weeks of March.
Age Requirement: 65-plus for the seniors' rate

Spectator Sports/Sporting Events

Edmonton Budweiser Motorsports Park
www.budpark.com
Event Hotline: 468-FAST (468-3278)

INFORMATION Edmonton Budweiser Motorsports Park is located near the international airport. Tickets can be purchased online.

SAVE Single ticket prices vary by event but seniors receive substantial discounts at the admission gate.
Age requirement: 65-plus

Edmonton Cracker Cats (Northern League Baseball)
www.crackercats.ca
Box Office: 423-BALL (423-2255)

INFORMATION The Edmonton Cracker Cats play at Telus Field from May to September. Wheelchair seating areas are available.

SAVE Good senior discounts are available. Grandstand tickets: Senior $8.50 (Adult $11.50). General Admission tickets: Senior $5.50 (Adult $8.50). Reserved Grandstand Season Tickets: Senior $350 (Adult $425). 15-Game Package: Senior $110 (Adult $135).
Age Requirement: 65-plus

University of Alberta Golden Bears and Pandas
www.uofaweb.ualberta.ca/athletics
429-BEAR (429-2327)

INFORMATION Bears and Pandas teams play football, volleyball, basketball and hockey. Games are held in various venues on the University of Alberta Campus.

SAVE Game-day single price tickets for all games are discounted for seniors.
Age Requirement: 65-plus

Consumer Shows

Edmonton's Rexall Place, Northlands Agricom and Sportex, and the Shaw Conference Centre regularly host large home and garden, vehicle, sports and lifestyle consumer shows. Senior age admission is generally $2 to $3 less than adult admission.

Bingos

Get those dabbers ready for B-I-N-G-O! There are various Senior Days and savings offered at bingo halls in Edmonton, St. Albert and Spruce Grove.

BINGOS – EDMONTON

Allendale Bingo
6120 – 104 Street; 430-9679

SAVE Tuesday and Wednesday evening and late night bingos are 1/2 price cards.

Age Requirement: Anyone

Caesar's Bingo
West Edmonton Mall; 444-3456

SAVE Monday is "1/2 Price Senior Day."

INFORMATION Operates seven days per week with afternoon, evening and late night bingos.

Age Requirement: 60-plus

Castledowns Bingo
12222 – 137 Avenue; 457-4670

SAVE Monday is "Senior Day" (all events 1/2 price excluding half-time).

INFORMATION Operates seven days per week with afternoon, evening and late night bingos. On Tuesday evenings, the first 100 customers receive a free meal from the full-menu concession.

Age Requirement: 60-plus

Crest Bingo
34 Street and 118 Avenue; 474-4670

SAVE Every Thursday is a "Seniors' Special"; besides $1 off cards, seniors receive several free cards including a Bonanza and an Early Bird.

Age Requirement: 60-plus

Edmonton North East Bingo
12711 – 52 Street; 476-0549

SAVE Thursday feature is "All you can play regular cards for $10."

Age Requirement: Anyone

Flamingo Bingo
148 Millbourne Shopping Centre; 466-3900
SAVE Mondays there are "1/2 price cards for seniors."
INFORMATION Afternoon and evening bingos.
Age Requirement: 60-plus

Kensington Bingo
12538 – 132 Avenue; 454-3635
SAVE Tuesday is "Senior 1/2 Price Day." Daily senior discount other days of $1 per senior customer.
INFORMATION Operates seven days per week with afternoon bingos. Monday is "Half-Price Ladies' Day" and Wednesday is "1/2 Price Everybody/Wacky Wednesday."
Age Requirement: 60-plus

Palm's Bingo
156 Street & Stony Plain Road; 483-1151
SAVE Seniors save $1 off on cards, always.
INFORMATION Evening bingos (seven evenings per week).
Age Requirement: 60-plus

Parkway Bingo
360, 8170 – 50 Street; 466-3541
SAVE Wednesday is "Senior Package Day."
INFORMATION Has afternoon, evening and late night bingos.
Age Requirement: 60-plus

Riviera Bingo
8775 – 51 Avenue; 465-1987
SAVE Tuesday is "Senior Day" (seniors receive regular game cards at 1/2 price). On all other days, seniors get $1 off cards.
INFORMATION Afternoon and evening bingos. Enquire about their advertised "Free Saturday Morning Bingo."
Age Requirement: 60-plus

West End Bingo Centre
17304 – 105 Avenue; 484-7228
SAVE "Senior Night" on Thursday (1/2 price cards).

INFORMATION Operates seven nights per week for evening bingo and afternoon bingo is offered on Saturdays and Sundays.
Age Requirement: 60-plus

BINGOS – ST. ALBERT

Campbell Park Bingo
20 Boudreau Road; 459-0103

SAVE Wednesday is "1/2 Price Senior Day."

INFORMATION Operates seven days per week. Morning, afternoon, evening and late night bingos offered. Morning bingo is offered Monday through Thursday only and late night bingo is offered Friday and Saturday only.
Age Requirement: 60-plus

BINGOS – SPRUCE GROVE

Spruce Grove Bingo
Hwy. 16A; 962-4040

SAVE Wednesday night is "Senior Night" ($5 package of cards free).

INFORMATION Operates seven days per week. Evening bingos seven days per week and afternoon bingos held on Saturdays, Sundays and holidays.
Age Requirement: 60-plus

Casinos

Be sure to see Chapter 1 *Food and Beverage* to learn about senior discounts in the restaurants at ABS Argyll Casino and ABS Yellowhead Casino.

ABS Argyll Casino
www.casinoabs.com
7055 Argyll Road; 463-9467

LOYALTY PROGRAM It is free to join Club West. Membership entitles you to earn points which can be redeemed for a wide variety of merchandise such as mugs, pens, and T-shirts. You receive 25 points plus a bonus of 50 points when you join. Every day that you visit, swipe your card at the Customer Service Desk to receive 25 points. You will receive 200 bonus points on your birthday if you visit the casino.

Mondays are double points for everyone who visits the casino and seniors receive triple points on Wednesdays. There are also "Bonus Days" and "Club Draws" periodically. You can only register one visit per day at each of the ABS Casino locations.

INFORMATION Your Club West Rewards Card can also be used in Edmonton at the ABS Yellowhead Casino, the ABS Casino in Calgary and the ABS Casino in Lethbridge.

Age Requirement for Club West: Anyone; 55-plus for triple points on Wednesdays.

ABS Yellowhead Casino

www.casinoabs.com

12464 – 153 Street; 424-9467

LOYALTY PROGRAM It is free to join Club West. Membership entitles you to earn points which can be redeemed for a wide variety of merchandise including mugs, pens, T-shirts etc. You receive 25 points plus a bonus of 50 points when you join. Every day that you visit, swipe your card at the Customer Service Desk to receive 25 points. You will receive 200 bonus points on your birthday if you visit the casino. Mondays are double points for everyone who visits the casino and seniors receive triple points on Wednesdays. There are also "Bonus Days" and "Club Draws" periodically. You can only register one visit per day at each of the ABS Casino locations.

INFORMATION Your Club West Rewards Card can also be used in Edmonton at the ABS Argyll Casino, at the ABS Casino in Calgary and the ABS Casino in Lethbridge.

Baccarat Casino

10128 – 104 Avenue; 413-3178

PROMOTION The third Monday of each month is "Super Seniors' Day." Senior customers can enjoy a full breakfast in the morning for $3.20 per person and they also receive a free deck of cards (while supplies last).

Age Requirement: 60-plus for "Super Seniors' Day"

Northlands Spectrum
www:thehorsesatnorthlands.com

78 Street and 115 Avenue; Player's Centre: 471-8174

INFORMATION It is free to join the Spectrum Players Club and you earn points each time you visit. Points can also be earned on handpay jackpots. There are also periodic free promotional games to earn points. Rewards include merchandise, play vouchers and food coupons. You can only register one visit per day for points. Members of the Spectrum Players Club receive *The Inside Edge* newsletter by mail every two months. Its contents include a listing of upcoming slot promotions and "clip 'n save" coupons for both the Colours and Uplinks restaurants in the casino.

PROMOTION: Every Monday is "Seniors' Day" with triple points on all jackpots, a chance to win $55 every half hour between 10:30 a.m. and 2:30 p.m. and one lucky senior has a chance of winning up to $100 cash at 2:30 p.m.
Age Requirement: 55-plus for "Seniors' Day"

Palace Casino
www.palacecasino.com

West Edmonton Mall (Upper Level Entrance 9); 444-2112

LOYALTY PROGRAM The Palace Casino Loyalty Club is free to join. Customers earn points each time they visit the casino; you can only register one visit per day. Points can be redeemed for merchandise including golf shirts and mugs and Palace Casino beverage/food discounts.

PROMOTION The last Monday of each month is "Super Seniors' Day." You'll find a coupon each month in the *Edmonton Senior* newspaper which entitles you to a $1 Free Play (you must present the coupon for this) and a breakfast special from 9 to 11:30 a.m. that is $2.95 per person.
Age Requirement: Anyone for the Palace Casino Loyalty Club; Age Requirement for the "Super Seniors' Day" free play and breakfast special: "senior" (see page XX).

Free Activities Especially For Seniors!

West Edmonton Mall 55+ Day

www.westedmall.com

55+ Day Telephone Hotline: 444-5250

FREE On the first Wednesday of February, April, June, September and November, West Edmonton Mall hosts 55+ Day, which features free entertainment and activities. To register, stop by the registration table located on Level One, in front of Zellers (near entrance #32) on 55+ Day.

More free activities are listed elsewhere in this chapter (for example, the Music Wednesdays At Noon series). Other chapters also contain information on free activities for seniors (e.g. details on the monthly Senior Day at the Tri-County Leisure Centre can be found in Chapter 4 *Fitness, Sports and Leisure*).

Chapter 3

Transportation

You will find that public transportation offers some very good senior discounts, whether you are taking public transit buses, Light Rail Transit (LRT) trains or hiring taxis.

The end of the chapter touches briefly on transportation options (and the discounts in those areas) if you are travelling out of Edmonton and area by coach, train, airplane or rental car.

Information for those seniors who own their own vehicle can be found in Chapter 9 *Automotive*.

Transit Systems

Well-run public transit systems exist in Edmonton, Sherwood Park and St. Albert. Although the community of Spruce Grove does not have a regular transit system, it does provide a non-profit door-to-door transportation service called Spruce Grove Specialized Transit Service. It is a reservation trip service for registered users (including seniors 55-plus) within Spruce Grove and the surrounding district. You can learn more about the program by contacting The City of Spruce Grove.

Here is information about the Edmonton Transit System (ETS), the Sherwood Park/Strathcona County Transit System and the transit system operated by the City of St. Albert:

Edmonton Transit System
www.edmonton.ca

Bus Link Telephone: 496-1600

SAVE Senior cash fare $1.75 (adult $2); senior day pass allowing unlimited travel on the bus or LRT $6 (adult same price); senior ticket book $13.50 (adult $16); senior monthly pass $11(Adult $59); and senior annual pass $105 (no adult annual pass category). Seniors who receive the Guaranteed Income Supplement are eligible to purchase an annual pass for $45. For information about seniors' passes call 496-1665. Note that first-time applicants must apply in person.

INFORMATION The ETS website has an ETS Trip Planner link from which you can get trip details specific to your needs. There is also a link entitled Bus Stop Schedule Search which is very convenient to use.

INFORMATION ETS also provides a Disabled Adult Transit Service (DATS); check with them for details. They also offer a free, customized travel training program for seniors and persons with mobility challenges, designed to advise Edmontonians about the range of accessibility options; call the Travel Training Centre for further information at 496-3000.
Age requirement: 65-plus for ETS senior pricing

Sherwood Park/Strathcona County Transit
www.strathcona.ab.ca
Telephone: 464-RIDE (464-7433)

SAVE Senior cash fare within Sherwood Park $2 (adult same price); senior cash fare commuter to/from Edmonton $2.50 (Adult $3.50); senior monthly pass within Sherwood Park $18 (adult $38); and senior annual pass within Sherwood Park plus commuter to/from Edmonton $216 (no adult annual pass category). Seniors who receive the Guaranteed Income Supplement are eligible to purchase an annual pass for $96.

INFORMATION Enquire about the Dial-A-Bus service which runs weekday evenings and Saturdays and Sundays.
Age Requirement: 65-plus for senior pricing

City of St. Albert Transit
www.city.st-albert.ab.ca

Customer Service Office: 459-6909

SAVE Senior bus fare within St. Albert $1.50 (adult $2.00); senior fare between St. Albert and Edmonton $2 (adult $3/$4 per trip); and senior monthly bus pass $21(Adult $70).

INFORMATION Regular bus service is provided within St. Albert and there is also commuter service to Edmonton. The fleet includes some low-floor and lift-equipped buses. The St. Albert Handibus Service is designed for those unable to use the regular transit system; call and enquire about details.
Age Requirement: 65-plus for senior pricing

Taxis

Taxis are a good transportation option for seniors. Most companies will take pre-arranged bookings so you are not telephoning the morning of an appointment (making it more convenient for you). Some fleets offer not only cars but mini-vans as well and if you have special requirements (e.g. wheelchair), enquire ahead of time. Many taxi companies offer flat rates to places such as the Edmonton International Airport.

Some taxi companies offer a discount off your fare while others sell books of coupons/vouchers that you purchase beforehand and use as cash to pay for fares (change is given in cash).

TAXI COMPANIES – EDMONTON

Capital Taxi
423-2425

SAVE $25 coupon/voucher booklets are available by pre-purchase and seniors pay $20 (amounting to a savings of 20 per cent). The coupon/voucher books can be ordered through the Capital Taxi office and picked up there.
Age Requirement: 55-plus

Co-Op Taxi
425-2525

SAVE There is a 10 per cent discount off the face value of coupon/voucher books and you can buy as many as you

require. They can be purchased at the Co-Op Taxi office or can be delivered to your home at no charge.
Age Requirement: Anyone

Yellow/Barrel/Checker and Prestige Cabs
- Yellow Cabs: 462-3456
- Barrel Taxi: 489-7777
- Checker Cabs: 484-8888
- Prestige Cabs: 462-4444

SAVE The parent company that operates these four cab/taxi companies offers a 20 per cent discount when seniors pre-purchase coupon/voucher books (e.g. a book of $25.00 taxi coupons/vouchers for $20.00). You can buy the coupon/voucher books at their head office or have them delivered to your home at no charge.
Age Requirement: 55-plus

TAXI COMPANIES – SHERWOOD PARK

AAA Sherwood Park Taxi
464-1333
SAVE Senior customers receive a 10 per cent discount on fares.
Age Requirement: 65-plus

Cabs In The Park
440-4444
SAVE Senior customers receive a 10 per cent discount on fares.
Age Requirement: 65-plus

TAXI COMPANIES – ST. ALBERT

St. Albert Taxi
459-5050
SAVE Senior customers receive a 10 per cent discount on fares.
Age Requirement: 60-plus

Sturgeon Cabs
458-8888
SAVE Senior customers receive a 10 per cent discount on fare.
INFORMATION This company often offers flat rates to their regular senior customers and they strive to pick-up senior citizens within 15 minutes of their telephone call.

Age Requirement: 65-plus

Heading "Out" of Edmonton...

Just a few paragraphs here about transportation for seniors heading out of Edmonton and area to visit family or to enjoy the sights.

Two major coach companies serve Edmonton: *Greyhound* (which operates throughout North America) and *Red Arrow Express* (which connects specific points in Alberta) are both very senior friendly and offer great senior fares. Here is their contact information:

Greyhound: www.greyhound.ca; 1-800-661-TRIP (1-800-661-8747)

Red Arrow: www.redarrow.pwt.ca; 1-800-232-1958

Transportation by train? *VIA Rail* offers some good savings on their fares for senior customers. Learn more by checking their website at www.viarail.ca or by contacting them by telephone at 1-888-VIA-RAIL (1-888-842-7245)

Renting a car or van? A good number of rental companies offer discounts to senior customers. Be sure to check around and don't hesitate to ask about senior discounts or senior pricing.

Travelling by air? Check with airlines directly (or through your travel agent) about the senior discount pricing that is available on some airlines.

Chapter 4

Fitness, Sports & Leisure

Fitness and sports opportunities are almost endless and include such activities as walking, swimming, skiing and golfing! The use of some fitness facilities is free while others are very affordable; and there are great senior discounts available.

If you want to learn more about becoming active, take a look at the interesting *"Active Edmonton"* website at www.activeedmonton.com. There is a link for older adults which further directs you to activity guidelines and other older adult links (active living and health resources on the web). There is also current information on fundraising runs happening in the Edmonton area (e.g. the annual Terry Fox Run).

Recreation and Fitness Centres

Today, you don't just go to the pool, the gym or the skating arena. Edmonton and surrounding communities have wonderful recreational centres which feature various combinations of pools, skating surfaces, fitness tracks and exercise rooms all under one roof.

There are great discounts for seniors – so keep fit and enjoy the offerings of these wonderful facilities!

RECREATION AND FITNESS CENTRES – EDMONTON

City of Edmonton Recreation Centres
www.edmonton.ca

General Information: 496-7946

INFORMATION There are thirteen facilities administered by the City of Edmonton, including the huge facilities of Kinsmen Centre, Commonwealth Fitness Centre and the Millwoods Recreation Centre. Other facilities include indoor pools and, in some cases, also outdoor running tracks and/or small indoor fitness centres. The City of Edmonton also administers several outdoor pools and they can provide information on these facilities which are open between late May and early September.

- A.C.T. Aquatic & Recreation Centre, 2909 – 113 Avenue in Rundle Park, 496-1494 (Note that the Hearing Impaired TTY Transfer Code for reaching this facility is "act.")
- Bonnie Doon Leisure Centre, 8648 – 81 Street, 496-1915
- Commonwealth Sports & Fitness Centre, 11000 Stadium Road, 944-7400
- Confederation Fitness & Leisure Centre, 11204 – 43 Avenue, 496-1488
- Eastglen Leisure Centre, 11410 – 68 Street; 496-7384
- Grand Trunk Fitness and Leisure Centre, 13025 – 112 Street, 496-8761
- Hardisty Fitness & Leisure Centre, 10535 – 65 Street, 496-1493
- Jasper Place Fitness & Leisure Centre, 9200 – 163 Street, 496-1411
- Kinsmen Sports Centre, 9100 Walterdale Hill, 944-7400
- Londonderry Fitness & Leisure Centre, 14528 – 66 Street, 496-7324
- Peter Hemmingway Fitness and Leisure Centre (formerly Coronation Fitness & Leisure Centre), 13808 – 111 Avenue, 496-1401
- Mill Woods Recreation Centre, 7207 – 28 Avenue, 496-2900 (Note that the Hearing Impaired TTY Transfer Code to reach this facility is "mwoods.")
- O'Leary Leisure Centre, 8804 – 132 Avenue, 496-7373

SAVE Admission plans are offered on a three-tier program.

- *Tier 1* is admission to all 13 city facilities.

- *Tier 2* is admission to 12 facilities (does not include Kinsmen Sports Centre).
- *Tier 3* is admission to 10 city facilities (does not include Kinsmen Sports Centre, Commonwealth Sports & Fitness Centre and the Mill Woods Recreation Centre).

Tier 1: Senior single admission $4.40 and Senior monthly admission $40.10 (Adult single admission $6.75 and Adult monthly admission $57.15). *Tier 2*: Senior single admission $4 and Senior monthly admission $33.30 (Adult single admission $5 and Adult monthly admission $48). *Tier 3*: Senior single admission $3.45 and Senior monthly admission $31.20 (Adult single admission $4.25 and Adult month admission $41.65). There is also senior pricing on all three tiers in terms of multi-admission options.
Age requirement for senior pricing: 65-plus

Grant MacEwan Centre for Sports and Wellness
www.macewan.ca
108 Street and 104 Avenue; 497-5300

INFORMATION This centre is becoming extremely well-known for its excellent 55-plus fitness classes including "55+ Stretch and Tone" held Mondays, "55+ Level 1 Fitness Classes" held on Tuesdays and Thursdays, and "55+ Level 2 Fitness Classes" held Wednesdays and Fridays. Each class is included with membership or there is a senior drop-in rate of $4 per person.

SAVE There are two types of memberships available. Plan A is an unlimited use membership and Plan B is a limited use membership (no "peak hour use" Monday to Friday between noon and 1 p.m. and 4:30 and 7 pm.). Plan A Senior $28 per month and Plan B Senior $24 per month (Plan A Adult $38.00 per month and Plan B Adult $30 per month). If you pay for 12 months in advance, you receive a 10 per cent discount off the monthly price. Drop-in rates are as follows: Senior day pass $4/$6 and Senior 10-visit pass $35 (Adult day pass $5.50/$8 and Adult 10-visit pass $50). Age Requirement for senior pricing: 55-plus

YMCA

www.edmonton.ymca.ca

INFORMATION If you join the Edmonton YMCA, you can use
the facilities at any of their locations in the city (there are
four of them, with a fifth soon to be under construction).
Seniors are provided with good savings on rates. It is important to note that new YMCA members are required to pay
a one-time Building Fee ($50 per person for "membership"
and $75 per person for "membership plus"). However,
the YMCA does not turn away those who are unable to
pay the full fee (further information available from the
YMCA Opportunity Fund). The "membership plus" option provides separate "adult only" facilities and additional
amenities/enhanced personalized services; enquire about
the extra costs association with this level of membership.
Offered as part of the "membership level" are:

- Aerobics programs in the gym and the pool
- Squash and racquetball court usage
- Fitness programs
- 50+ programs
- Swim instruction
- Tai chi and yoga
- Use of day lockers

SAVE Senior annual pass $464 (Adult $518) or monthly $43 and
$48 respectively. Note that all memberships are reduced
by 10 per cent when paying for 12 months in advance. If
your spouse would also like an annual pass, he/she pays
$367(Adult spouse $400).
Age Requirement for senior pricing: 65-plus

- Castle Downs YMCA, 11510 – 153 Avenue; 476-YMCA
  (476-9622)
- Jamie Platz YMCA, 7121 – 178 Street; 481-YMCA (481-
  9622)
- William Lutsky YMCA, 1975 – 111 Street; 469-3367
- Downtown YMCA, 10030 – 102 A Avenue; 421-YMCA
  (421-9622)

- A new Don Wheaton Family YMCA, to be constructed at 103 Street and 102 Avenue (downtown), has just been announced!

RECREATION AND FITNESS CENTRES – SHERWOOD PARK

Glen Allen Rec Complex
199 Georgian Way; 467-4404
(fitness and indoor skating)

Kinsmen Leisure Centre
2001 Oak Street; 464-2112
(swimming pool only)

Millennium Place
2000 Premier Way; 416-3300
(indoor fitness track, fitness centre and pool)
www.strathcona.ab.ca

INFORMATION These three facilities offer recreational and fitness opportunities to Strathcona County residents. The Millennium Card allows access to all three facilities. Note that information about indoor skating opportunities at the Glen Allen Rec Complex and costs is found elsewhere in this chapter under "Skating – Indoor".

SAVE Millennium Card: This card allows you to use all three Sherwood Park facilities. You can pay through monthly preauthorized payments or an annual payment plan. Senior $27 per month with second adult from same family $21.50 (Adult $32 with second senior from same family $27).

SAVE Glen Allen Recreation Complex: fitness Single visit senior $3.50 (Adult $4.50); one month pass Senior $27 (Adult $32); three months Senior $64.80 (Adult $76.80); and annual Senior $210.60 (Adult $249.60).

SAVE Kinsmen Leisure Centre: swimming single visit Senior $3.25 (Adult $4.50). There are adult swim public times to choose from and the Young At Heart 55+ Program time slots run several times per week.

SAVE Millennium Place: swimming single visit Senior $5.25 (Adult $8.50).
Age Requirement for senior pricing: 65-plus

RECREATION AND FITNESS CENTRES – ST. ALBERT

INFORMATION Plans have been announced for a huge new multi-purpose recreation centre to be built in St. Albert!

Fountain Park Recreation Centre
www.stalbert.ca
    4 Cunningham Road; 459-1553

INFORMATION Offered are swim classes and aqua fitness programs in this swimming facility.

SAVE Admission fee per swim: Senior $3.25 (Adult $4). Senior pricing offered on 10, 20 and 30-coupon options as well as one, three, six and 12 month passes.

INFORMATION Enquire about the 50+ Club morning swim classes and drop-in aqua fitness programs. The leisure pool has wheelchair ramp access.
    Age Requirement for senior pricing: 60-plus

RECREATION AND FITNESS CENTRES – SPRUCE GROVE/STONY PLAIN

Trans-Alta Tri Leisure Centre
www.trileisure.com
    221 Campsite Road in Spruce Grove; 960-5060

INFORMATION Residents of Spruce Grove, Stony Plain and Parkland County can take advantage of this recreational complex.

FREE "Senior Day" is the second Wednesday of each month (60-plus) from 10 a.m. to 3 p.m. Seniors can attend free and are encouraged to bring along their own musical instrument and enjoy a "jamming session" from 10 a.m. to 1 p.m. During the rest of the afternoon there is a birthday celebration, a fit break and a guest speaker with complimentary refreshments served. Seniors who participate in the drop-in activities at the leisure centre during day are required to pay the drop-in fee.

SAVE Daily admission Senior $5.75 (Adult $6.75). Annual individual membership Senior $333.50 with a second senior under family pricing structure $268.00 (Adult $399.00 with a second adult under family pricing structure $333.50). Punch cards (10 visit pass) Senior $48.50 (Adult $58.30).

Age Requirement for senior pricing: 60-plus

RECREATION AND FITNESS CENTRES – LEDUC

Black Gold Centre
980-7120

INFORMATION The Black Gold Centre facility combines opportunities for swimming and opportunities for skating. A "fitness" admission or pass gives access to lane swim, aquafit, public swim and public skate while a "leisure" admission or pass gives access to lane swim, aquafit, public swim, public skate and waterslide/children's play area.

SAVE Individual admissions: Senior fitness $3 (Adult $4) and Senior leisure $4.25 (Adult $5.25). Punch cards for 10 admissions: Senior fitness $27 (Adult $36) and Senior leisure $38.25 (Adult $47.25). Monthly passes: Senior fitness $18 (Adult $24) and Senior leisure $25.50 (Adult $31.50). Annual passes: Senior fitness $211 (Adult $281) and Senior leisure $299 (Adult $369).
Age Requirement for senior pricing: 65-plus

Bowling For Fun & Exercise!

Bowling is particularly popular during the fall, winter and early spring months. Many bowling lanes and centres have senior leagues made up of seniors who bowl together on a regular basis; there is generally great pricing on games and shoe rental and most leagues have a social/fun component including a wind-up banquet.

SAVE Many bowling lanes and centres participate in the *"Show Your Card & Save Program"* and you can save if you are a member of the Alberta Motor Association.

Listed here are bowling lanes and centres in Edmonton and area; the price for one game of public bowling is shown (shoes are always extra) and the age requirement for the senior pricing is also indicated. Public bowling times vary from facility to facility due to their booked league play, so telephone and enquire beforehand about public bowling times and lane availability.

BOWLING – EDMONTON

- *Bonnie Doon Bowling Lanes:* Bonnie Doon Mall, 466-9047 (Senior $3.50 and Adult $3.75; 55-plus for senior pricing)
- *Bronx Bowling Centre:* 12940 – 127 Street, 455-2366 (Senior $4.25 and Adult $4.50; 55-plus for senior pricing)
- *Fraser Bowling Centre:* 2603 – 151 Avenue, 478-5955 (Senior before 6 p.m. $2.50/after 6 p.m. $3.75; and Adult before 6 p.m. $2.75/after 6 p.m. $4; 55-plus for senior pricing)
- *Gateway Entertainment Centre*: 3414 Gateway Boulevard, 435-1922 (senior pricing offered on 9 a.m. to 6 p.m. time category, 6 to 9 p.m. time category and 9 p.m. to close time category; 55-plus for senior pricing)
- *KJ Bowl*: 12143 – 54 Street, 477-3132 (Senior $3 and adult $3.50; 55-plus for senior pricing)
- *Plaza Bowl*: 10418 – 118 Avenue, 477-7848 (Senior $2.75 and Adult $3.25; senior pricing for "senior" – (see page XX)

BOWLING – SHERWOOD PARK

- *Sherwood Park Bowl*: 975 Fir Street, 464-2100 (Senior $3.75 and Adult $4; 55-plus for senior pricing)

BOWLING – ST. ALBERT

- *St. Albert Bowling Centre*: 14 Inglewood Drive, 459-3337 (senior pricing offered on both five-pin and 10-pin bowling always; 55-plus for senior pricing)

BOWLING – SPRUCE GROVE

- *Tee and T Lanes*: 125 South Avenue, 962-9097 (Senior $3.25 and Adult $4 plus a "Drop-In Seniors' Bowl" each Friday at 1 p.m. where senior bowlers play three games for $5; 55-plus for senior pricing)

BOWLING – LEDUC

- *Leduc Lanes*: 6609 – 45 Street, 986-3502 (anyone can bowl for a full hour (including your shoe rental) for $7 per person; you can reserve lanes ahead of time for public bowling slots)

Walking Is Good Exercise!

Walking is considered one of the best exercises, and if you run or jog, you can derive many of its benefits even more quickly. The outdoor trail system provides many opportunities for an enjoyable walk and the good news is that these trails are free to use. Some additional walking opportunities are listed in Chapter 8 under "walking tours" for Sherwood Park, Stony Plain and Leduc.

A new initiative of the City of Edmonton is their newsletter *"Taking Steps... towards a more walkable Edmonton."* This newsletter can be e-mailed to you at no charge or you can ask to have a print copy of it mailed to you. For more info see the City of Edmonton website, www.edmonton.ca.

WALKING – EDMONTON

- *Edmonton's river valley parks system* is vast. For details check the City of Edmonton website at www.edmonton.ca. The central jogging loop, routes running east and west from Kinsmen Park can be utilized during the winter months, too. Further information: 496-2950.
- In downtown Edmonton, good places to access the trail system are the **Alberta Legislature Grounds** and **Louise McKinney Park** (adjacent to the Shaw Conference Centre).

WALKING – ST. ALBERT

- The City of St. Albert has **Red Willow Park**, running the full length of the river valley and conveniently connected to neighbourhoods – 45 kilometres of walking trails. Further information: 459-1557.

WALKING – SPRUCE GROVE

- Spruce Grove's **Heritage Grove Park Trail System** offers trails to enjoy. For further information call The City of Spruce Grove at 962-7619 or log onto their website at www.sprucegrove.org.

WALKING – STONY PLAIN

- The Town of Stony Plain's trail system has over 14.5 kilometres of asphalt trails and it is maintained on a year-round basis. One of the parks on the trail system is

Whispering Waters Park. Further information is available on www.stonyplain.com.

Indoor Health Walk Loops

The Alberta Legislature pedway offers *"Health Walk Loops"* – a joint venture of the Legislative Assembly Office and the Grant MacEwan College Centre for Sports and Wellness. Check www.assembly.ab.ca for information on these walking loops. They are open from 6 a.m. to 6 p.m. weekdays; and on weekends/ holidays between October 16 to April 30 from noon to 5 p.m.; and between May 1 and October 15 from 9 a.m. to 5 p.m. Located in downtown Edmonton at 10820 – 98 Avenue – telephone 427-7362.

Mall Walking Groups/Opportunities

Seniors are indeed fortunate that Edmonton and area shopping malls provide mall walking opportunities – considering what the weather conditions can be like between late September and May! Mall walking during these months gives you the opportunity to enjoy this form of activity in a climate-controlled environment, as you would do outdoors during June, July and August. Designated walking hours are prior to opening of the mall stores so there are no crowds to contend with. You can pick your days and the specific times during the mall walking hours that work for you. It's good exercise and there is often a chance to socialize afterwards with other walkers over a coffee and muffin in the food court area.

Here are mall walking opportunities (for free!) in Edmonton and area. Note that malls that have specified "clubs" usually only run their programs between September and May (or April in some cases):

MALL WALKING – EDMONTON

Bonnie Doon Shopping Centre
Whyte Avenue and 83 Street; 465-7902

INFORMATION This mall's new program is coordinated by the seniors' group located here. Members will greet you every weekday morning (Monday to Friday) just outside Zellers (use Entrance 2 on the east side to enter mall) and register you, take your coat at the coat check and help you record your daily distances; 8 a.m. to 10 a.m. The program runs year round.

Londonderry Mall
137 Avenue and 66 Street; 475-9266

INFORMATION This is the largest mall walking club in Edmonton, with more than 1,000 participants. It is free to join the "Walk 'N Roll Mall Walking Program" which runs Monday to Friday mornings from 7 a.m. to 10 a.m. When you register as a member you will receive free lap tracking cards, newsletters, exclusive walking T-shirts, motivational rewards, a discount for members at participating stores (with your club ID) and fitness tips. There are also fun activities and theme days every month!

Mill Woods Town Centre
2331 – 66 Street; 461-2400

INFORMATION The mall administration will provide you with a contact for the group of regular mall walkers. Walkers can enter at any entrance and you can set your own pace. The mall walking route length is 1.1 kilometres; you can walk some or all of the route. Most walkers walk between the hours of 7:30 and 10 a.m. and meet for coffee in the food court around 9 a.m. Mall walkers are asked to register at one of the daily coffee meets. Several times per year, the mall administration hosts coffee parties for mall walkers.

Northgate Centre
137 Avenue and 97 Street; 475-3695

INFORMATION You can join this mall walking club at the Administration Office, upstairs by the food court (September to May). 7 a.m. to 10 a.m. daily. Club members receive a log book, and free items are awarded by the mall administration and tenants for certain goals reached!

Southgate Centre
51 Avenue and 111 Street; 435-3721

INFORMATION The Southgate Centre Walker's Club runs seven
days per week for the two hours prior to mall opening
(8 a.m. to 10 a.m. Monday to Friday; 7:30 to 9:30 a.m.
Saturday; and 9 to 11 a.m. on Sunday). Walkers can register every second Tuesday of the month with volunteers at
the Customer Service Centre (you can also register on days
other than the second Tuesday of the month if you cannot
attend the designated Tuesday). Each club member is provided with a free log book, with incentives given for com-
pleting sections of this log book, as well as a list of retailers
at which walkers can obtain discounts and tenant coupons.

West Edmonton Mall
87 Avenue and 170 Street; 444-5200

INFORMATION West Edmonton Mall provides a course of
some six kilometres (Level One is equivalent to 3.3 kilometres and Level Two is equivalent to 2.8 kilometres).
Recommended mall-walking hours are 7 a.m. to 10 a.m.
any day.

MALL WALKING – SHERWOOD PARK

Sherwood Park Mall
2020 Sherwood Drive; 467-7766

INFORMATION Mall walkers are welcomed seven days a week
between 7 a.m. and 9:30 a.m. (later starting hours on
Sundays). Enter at the Safeway/Mall entrance on the west
side.

MALL WALKING – ST. ALBERT

St. Albert Centre
St. Albert Road and Bellerose Drive; 458-7882

INFORMATION The St. Albert Centre Mallwalkers Club meets
Monday to Friday mornings between 7:30 and 9:30 a.m.
(you can "come and go" for the time slot within these two
hours that works for you). You can register as a club member with the mall administration. Mall walkers can gain
access to the mall through Entrance #2.

Downhill Skiing in Edmonton & Area

Locally, there are some great choices for downhill skiing and some incredible savings!

Edmonton Ski Club

www.edmontonskiclub.com

Located in the river valley at 9613 – 96 Avenue; 465-0852

SAVE Seniors really save big on season memberships, paying $42 for the season (Adult season membership $199). And, if you pay before September 30, you will receive 10 per cent off; before October 31 you will receive five per cent off! Age Requirement: 55-plus

Rabbit Hill

www.rabbithill.com

Off Highway 19, near Devon; 955-2440

SAVE Senior daily rate: $15 (three hours or less), $18 (five hours or less), $20 (unlimited hours) and $11 (week nights after 6 p.m.); the comparable Adult pricing in these categories: $22, $27, $30, and $16. Flexi-Pass (six full-day totally transferable day passes): Senior $95 (Adult $125). Age Requirement: 65-plus

Snow Valley

www.snowvalley.ab.ca

119 Street off Whitemud Drive; 434-3991

SAVE Day passes: Seniors get a great price at $9 (for all categories); Adult $20 (three hours or less), $22 (five hours or less), $24 (full day) and $7 (last two hours). A senior season's pass is $49 (Adult $194.65). Age Requirement: 55-plus

Sunridge

www.sunridgeskiarea.com

Four blocks south of the Yellowhead on 17 Street; 449-6555

SAVE Senior all-day lift ticket $11.00 (Adult all-day lift ticket $24.00 and Adult 3 hours or less $20.00). Age Requirement: 55-plus

Cross Country Skiing in the Edmonton Area

This sport is truly an excellent form of exercise and certainly fun for all ages! Edmonton's river valley parks offer a spectacular 50-kilometres-plus of groomed trails. You can obtain (free of charge) a brochure entitled *Cross Country Ski Guide* from the River Valley Rangers at Victoria Park during ski season or call 446-4314. The map outlines beginner, intermediate and advanced trails and marks where washrooms, parking and telephones are located in each area.

General hours of these parks are 8 a.m. to 10 p.m. There is no charge to ski these cross-country trails:

- *Capilano Park* (south bank of the river west of 50 Street)
- *Gold Bar Park* (east of 50 Street and north of 109 Avenue)
- *Kinsmen Park* (base of Walterdale Hill on the south side of the 105 Street Bridge)
- *Mill Creek Park* (Argyll Park down to Connors Road)
- *Riverside Golf Course* (Rowland Road and 84 Street)
- *Terwillegar Park* (Rabbit Hill Road and into the river valley)
- *Victoria Park* (River Valley Road and east of Groat Road)
- *William Hawrelak Park* (west side of Groat Road, south of the Groat Road Bridge)

Downhill Skiing in the Mountains

It is pretty likely that each ski season, enthusiasts will head to the mountains for at least one resort excursion. And the good news is that senior lift ticket pricing is available at these mountain resorts, which are just hours away. You can check their websites for further information:

- *Banff: Lake Louise,* www.skilouise.com or call (403) 256-8473 (65-plus)
- *Banff: Norquay,* www.banffnorquay.com or call (403) 762-4421 (65-plus)
- *Banff: Sunshine Village,* www.skibanff.com or call 1-87SKI-BANFF Toll Free (65-plus)
- *Jasper: Marmot Basin,* www.skimarmot.com or call 1-866-952-3816 Toll Free (65-plus)

- *Canmore: Fortress Mountain,* www.skifortress.ca or call (403) 591-7108 (60-plus)
- *Canmore: Nakiska,* www.skinakiska.com or call 1-800-258-7669 Toll Free (65-plus)

Indoor Skating

INDOOR SKATING – EDMONTON

The City of Edmonton/The Kinsmen Club of Edmonton

FREE Public skating is available free at all city arenas and the Kinsmen arena (the free public skating maximum is 100 skaters at each location). Public skating times are different for each location, with some time slots, generally an hour in duration, on weekday afternoons and evenings and others on the weekend. You can learn more about the arenas and public skating times on The City of Edmonton website at www.edmonton.ca or by calling 496-4999.
Age Requirement: Anyone

Ice Palace at West Edmonton Mall

87 Avenue and 170 Street; 444-5300

AFFORDABLE The "Senior 55-plus Skate Program" runs from 10 a.m. to 11 a.m. weekday mornings. The cost for seniors is $2.25 for the hour. Public skating at the Ice Palace takes place at various times; check with them directly. Admission is senior $2.95 (Adult $4.95).
Age Requirement for senior pricing: 55-plus

Westmount Shopping Centre Indoor Skating Facility

111 Avenue and Groat Road; 452-1234

AFFORDABLE On Monday, Wednesday and Friday mornings, there is a "55-plus Senior Skate" between 9 and 10 a.m. The cost per person is $3.
Age Requirement: 55-plus

INDOOR SKATING – SHERWOOD PARK

Glen Allen Recreation Complex

199 Georgian Way; 467-4404

AFFORDABLE "Seniors' Skate" from 2 to 3 p.m. with refreshments following, at $2 per person, per time.

Age Requirement: "Senior" (see page 3)

Millennium Place

Yellowhead Trail and Broadmoor Boulevard; 416-3300

GOOD VALUE There are many time slots for public skating.
Included with your paid facility admission.
Age Requirement: Anyone

INDOOR SKATING – ST. ALBERT

Kinex Arena

Telephone: 459-1568 or 459-1600

AFFORDABLE There is public skating available on Mondays and
Wednesday evenings between 7 and 8 p.m.; Saturdays from
1 to 2 p.m.; and Sundays from 1:45 to 3:15 p.m. Senior
single admission is $2.25; 10-pass admission $18; 20-pass
admission $32; and 30-pass admission $42 (Adult $3, $27,
$48 and $63). The first Saturday of each month is "Cheap-
Skates" – senior admission for public skating is a loonie.
Age Requirement: "Senior" (see page 3)

INDOOR SKATING – SPRUCE GROVE

Agrena

Telephone 962-2031

FREE Public skating Monday to Friday between 11:30 a.m. and
12:30 p.m. is free; it is sponsored by the Spruce Grove
Kinsmen.
Age Requirement: Anyone

INDOOR SKATING – LEDUC

Black Gold Arena

Telephone 980-7120

FREE Public skating is free Wednesday evenings between 6:15
p.m. and 7:15 p.m.; and Sundays between 12:45 p.m. and
2:30 p.m.
Age Requirement: Anyone

Outdoor Skating

Some neighbourhoods allow public skating on their outdoor
rinks. Watch for publicity from the community league about when
these open for the season. There is also public outdoor skating on

ice surfaces at Edmonton's City Hall and the Alberta Legislature grounds.

Cycling

The City of Edmonton produces a great brochure entitled *Cycle Edmonton*. The brochure has a map for cyclists to help them choose the best route according to their ability and there is also information on biking in the river valley parks. Check the website at www.edmonton.ca for further information or call 496-4999.

The website of the *Juventus Cycling Club* (www.juventus.ab.ca) indicates that an annual membership for those 70 years of age and over is free! You can contact this club at 490-5979.

Golf Courses... Fore!

It's common knowledge that there are some prime golf courses in Edmonton and surrounding area. No matter whether you're a beginning golfer or a pro, golfing is an enjoyable sport during the spring, summer and early-autumn months.

A great deal of information is contained in the golf sections in spring and summer issues of the monthly *Edmonton Senior* newspaper. Edmonton Tourism publishes an annual *Greater Edmonton Visitors' Guide* (free) which includes a comprehensive section on golf courses in metro Edmonton and those outside the city which could be done as a day trip. Travel Alberta can provide you with a free copy of the *Golfer's Guide* (Alberta and British Columbia).

There are a number of golf courses which offer a senior discount or senior specials. Here are some:

Edmonton

Raven Crest Golf & Country Club 408-8687
River Ridge Golf & Country Club 408-8687
Lewis Estates Golf Course 489-4653
Millwoods Golf Course 448-1601
Sandpiper Golf & Country Club 408-8687
The Ranch Golf & Country Club 421-9201
Twin Willows Golf Course 447-2934
Dragon's Head Par 3 Golf Club 944-4653

Edmonton Springs Golf Club 962-6500
Fox Run Golf Course 998-4653
Pioneer Meadows Golf Course 988-8375
Red Tail Landing Golf Club 890-7888
Whitemud Creek Golf Resort 988-6800
Oaks Golf Club 988-8000
Golden West Golf Course 447-1099
Goose Hummock Golf Resort 421-7222
Sturgeon Valley Golf & Country Club 973-6700
Grouse Nest Golf Course 892-2006
Jagare Ridge Golf Course 432-4030

Sherwood Park

Legacy Ridge Golf Course 464-7545
Sherwood Park Golf Course 467-5060
Legends Golf & Country Club 449-4911
Northern Bear Golf Club 922-2327
Broadmoor Golf Course 467-7373

Leduc

Leduc Golf & Country Club 986-2803

Fort Saskatchewan

Fort-In-View Golf Course 998-1234

St. Albert

Coyote Canyon Golf Course 460-1311
Indian Lakes Golf Club 470-4653
Terra Pines Golf Course 458-1122
J R Golf Course 459-8735

Wabamun

Ironhead Golf & Country Club 892-4653
Cougar Creek Golf Resort 892-4545

Spruce Grove

Deer Meadows Golf Course 962-4799
Links at Spruce Grove 962-4653

Devon

Devon Golf & Country Club 987-3569
Westridge Park Lodge 987-4885

Stony Plain

Duffy's Challenge Golf Course 968-7654
Stony Plain Golf Course 963-2133

Beaumont

Eagle Rock Golf Course 464-4653

Chapter 5

Hobbies

Ah, hobbies! Perhaps during your entire lifetime you've been involved in a hobby like reading, woodworking or drawing. Or has hands-on crafting always been an interest of yours? Maybe you're looking to learn about and get involved in a new hobby?

This chapter will provide some good resource information regarding a large number of hobbies ranging from scrapbooking to lapidary, and some discounts on supplies.

Scrapbooking

Scrapbooking has become very popular these past few years and there are many retail stores to shop at for supplies.

All the Edmonton and area scrapbooking stores listed here offer some type of "loyalty card stamp club" or "frequent buyers card" and, although the concept of the cards is basically the same (receive stamps for purchases made and when card is full, receive a discount or money off on your next purchase and then start a new card), each program varies slightly so check with each individual store. Any customer can participate. Also note that at some shops, purchases of sale items do not qualify for stamps.

A Scrapper's Delight
#75 South Avenue in Spruce Grove; 960-4229
INFORMATION Enquire about their "Scrapbucks Promotion," held four times annually.

Creative Scrapbooks
120, 17010 – 90 Avenue in Edmonton; 944-1441

Memory Lane Scrapbook Supplies
7, 4922 – 51 Avenue in Leduc; 980-0100

Scrapbook Adventures
105, 8170 50 Street in Edmonton, 490-4229

INFORMATION Mondays are "double stamp days," and on your birthday receive a 20 per cent discount on purchases!

Scrapbook Corner
142, 1020 Sherwood Drive in Sherwood Park; 464-0284

Scrapbook Memories & More
20, 975 Broadmoor Baseline Crossing in Sherwood Park; 449-060

Urban Scrapbooking
14315 – 118 Avenue in Edmonton; 451-3459

Scrap A Lot
9218 – 51 Avenue in Edmonton, 944-1526

LOYALTY PROGRAM It costs $2 to obtain a "Key Tag Loyalty Program" card with which customers receive 10 per cent off after a certain monetary amount in purchases; customers can then obtain a new card for $2. There is a monthly draw of redeemed key tag cards for a $100 gift certificate.

Astronomy

TELUS World of Science (formerly Odyssium)
FREE If you have an interest in astronomy, check out the website (www.odyssium.com) and access the "Astronomy Info" link. On it you'll find information on:
- Our Observatory
- Astronomical Events
- Collector's Space Card Program
- Space Links
- Night Photos

- Be A Star

Lapidary

Bedrock Supply
9435 – 63 Avenue in Edmonton; 434-2040
SAVE Regular customers receive a 10 per cent discount on dis-
countable items within the store, every day.
Age Requirement: Anyone

Drawing and Painting

Colours at Nordraft Art Supplies
SAVE Seniors get a 10 per cent discount, every day, on art supplies (picture framing excluded).

LOCATED IN EDMONTON
- 10660 – 105 Street; 426-7820
- 10818 – 82 Avenue; 433-4774
- 10104 – 149 Street; 481-6950
Age Requirement: 65-plus

Delta Art & Drafting Supply
11116 – 120 Street in Edmonton; 455-7983
SAVE Seniors get a 10 per cent discount, every day, on art supplies.
Age Requirement: 65-plus

Paint for Joy!
www.paint4joy.com
#107, 23 Atkins Drive in St. Albert; 418-3488
SAVE Seniors receive a 10 per cent discount on painting supplies
every Tuesday.
Age Requirement: 60-plus

The Paint Spot
www.paintspot.ca
10516 Whyte Avenue; 432-0240
SAVE 10 per cent discount, always, on artist painting supplies.
Age Requirement: 65-plus

Art Classes

If you check the website for *Artistically Speaking School of Fine Art* at www.artisticallyspeaking.ab.ca, you will see that "senior discounts" are offered on classes; you will need to speak to them directly regarding the range of classes they offer, times classes are run and what age you need to be to benefit from the senior discounts. Enquire about their "ticket book of ten classes," especially for people who cannot commit to a weekly time schedule. They can be reached at 487-6559 and they are located in the Primrose Lane Shopping Centre in west Edmonton at 8446 -182 Street.

Sewing and Hands-On Crafting

Many seniors enjoy sewing and/or designing and creating handcrafts. Here are some stores where you can get materials for sewing and items you need for crafting at great savings!

Fabricland

www.fabriclandwest.com

1-866-R-FABRIC (1-866-732-2742)

INFORMATION Anyone can join the Fabricland Sewing Club and receive discounts, member pricing and notice of exclusive sales events. The "Shop, Stamp and Save" stamp-card program means you can save even more on purchases.

SAVE Senior annual membership $12 and Senior three-year membership $27 (Adult annual memberships $15 and Adult three-year membership $30).

LOCATED IN EDMONTON

- 5357 Gateway Boulevard; 438-5119
- 10104 – 175 Street; 444-1908
- Mill Woods Town Centre; 462-2160
- Londonderry Mall; 478-0435
- Located in Sherwood Park:
- #128 270 Baseline Road; 467-0822

LOCATED IN ST. ALBERT

- 215 Carnegie Drive; 460-9136

LOCATED IN LEDUC

- 5205 – 50 Avenue; 986-6969
  Age Requirement: 60-plus for senior membership pricing category.

Lewiscraft
www.lewiscraft.ca

LOCATED IN EDMONTON

- Bonnie Doon Shopping Centre; 468-6650
- Kingsway Garden Mall; 471-1775
- Londonderry Mall; 475-5732
- West Edmonton Mall; 444-1391

LOCATED IN SHERWOOD PARK

- Sherwood Park Mall; 416-0399

INFORMATION Their flyers have great coupons!

SAVE Lewiscraft stores offer a promotion that any crafter can benefit from! For a $7 annual fee (good for one year from the month of purchase), you will receive a keychain membership card that entitles you to receive a seven per cent discount. On "Seniors' Day," every Monday, senior customers receive 10 per cent off regularly-priced purchases. This discount can be combined with the seven per cent membership discount for a total savings of 17 per cent on purchases made on "Seniors' Day".
Age Requirement: Anyone for membership and 65-plus for "Seniors' Day" discount.

Growing Plants & Orchids

Edmonton's **Muttart Conservatory** has a website with great fact sheets about plants (from jade trees to gerberas) that you will find useful if you enjoy growing things. You can access their website at www.edmonton.ca/muttart.

The **Devonian Botanic Garden** provides a link on their website entitled *The Green Zone* (www.devonian.ualberta.ca). You'll find:

- Garden growing tips;
- Horticultural books for sale;
- A seed list catalogue;

- Links to other botanic gardens around North America; and
- Ask An Expert: Edmonton area zone, zone 2 and zone 3.

The *Orchid Species Presentation Foundation* has a great website that contains much orchid information including description, names and history. The website address is www.orchidspecies.ca.

Travel

Are travelling and sightseeing your hobby? Several times per year, *Jenode Tours* (452-2361) – which specializes in motorcoach travel and excursions – holds free travel show events in Central Lions Senior Centre and the Northgate Lions Senior Centre auditoriums. You'll be treated to free coffee and there are draws to enter! Call Jenode Tours to see when the next travel show event is scheduled for.

Remember that the following loyalty programs earn you points towards free travel:
- Aeroplan Miles (Air Canada)
- Air Miles Program
- Sky High Points Program through purchases at Save On Food grocery stores

Reading is a Great Hobby

Public libraries are great places for people of all ages! And if reading is a hobby of yours, your annual library membership will be of great value. The libraries listed here serve the residents of the geographical area they are situated in; if you are a non-resident of the area, you will be paying for a library card under a different category.

Many branches sponsor senior-friendly events such as weekly book clubs. And besides fiction and non-fiction books to borrow, today's libraries offer great selections of newspapers and magazines, CDs and DVDs, plus videos. Some libraries offer a great selection of large print books and some offer patrons the use of magnifying readers on-site. Also, you can often book computer time to work on a project or to surf the web; each library has rules about length of access time per patron in place.

LIBRARIES – EDMONTON
Edmonton Public Library
www.epl.ca

INFORMATION There are 15 branches within the Edmonton Public Library system. The main one is the Stanley A. Milner library branch downtown. Most branches have 24-hour return bins (with the exception of shopping mall branches located at Abbottsfield Mall, Capilano Mall, Londonderry Mall and Mill Woods Town Centre). The library has an extremely comprehensive website and the home page allows you to navigate to various links including *"55 & Better," "Databases"* and *"Personalized Book List,"* to name a few.

Branch locations:
- Calder Branch, 12522 – 132 Avenue, 496-7090
- Capilano Branch, in Capilano Shopping Centre at 5004 – 98 Avenue, 496-1802
- Castle Downs Branch, 106 Lake Side Landing at 15379 Castledowns Road, 496-1804
- Highlands Branch, 6710 – 118 Avenue, 496-1806
- Idylwylde Branch, 8310 – 88 Avenue, 496-1808
- Jasper Place Branch, 9010 – 156 Street, 496-1810
- Lessard Branch, in Lessard Shopping Centre at 6104 – Callingwood Road, 496-1871
- Mill Woods Branch, in Mill Woods Town Centre, 496-1818
- Penny McKee Branch, Abbottsfield Shoppers Mall, 496-7839
- Riverbend Branch, 460 Riverbend Square, 944-5311
- Sprucewood Branch, 11555 – 95 Street, 496-7099
- Stanley A. Milner Library, downtown at 7 Sir Winston Churchill Square, 496-7000
- Strathcona Branch, 7506 Gateway Boulevard, 496-1828
- Whitemud Crossing Branch, 145 Whitemud Crossing at 4211 – 106 Street, 496-1822
- Londonderry Branch, 110 Londonderry Mall, 496-1814
- Woodcroft Branch, 13420 – 114 Avenue, 496,1830

GREAT VALUE Annual borrower's fee: first adult per household $12 and additional adult $8. You may use your library card at any branch of the Edmonton Public Library system.

LIBRARIES – SHERWOOD PARK

Strathcona County Public Library
www.sclibrary.ab.ca
> 2020 Sherwood Drive (east side of Sherwood Park Mall); 449-5800

INFORMATION There is a vast selection of talking and large print books in their collection. "Vacation loans" may be arranged by consulting the Circulation Desk staff.

GREAT VALUE Annual borrowing fee is $12 for any age and additional borrower $3.
> Age Requirement: Anyone

LIBRARIES – ST. ALBERT

St. Albert Public Library
www.sapl.ab.ca
> St. Albert Place; 459-1530

INFORMATION St. Albert Place is fully accessible for wheelchairs; there is an elevator in the library to reach the Adult Services Department on the second floor.

SAVE Senior family annual library card $20 (Family annual library card $30).
> Age Requirement for senior family category: 65-plus

LIBRARIES – SPRUCE GROVE

Spruce Grove Public Library
www.sprucegrovelibrary.org
> #15, 420 King Street; 962-4423

INFORMATION Make enquires about some great programs they offer, including a monthly book club, a "Stitch 'n Chat" group which meets monthly, and "Senior's Storytelling."

SAVE Library card annual fees: senior $8 (Adult $15).
> Age Requirement for senior category: 65-plus

LIBRARIES – STONY PLAIN

Stony Plain Public Library
www.stonyplainlibrary.org.

4613 – 52 Avenue in Forest Green Plaza; 963-5440

INFORMATION Enquire about the Afternoon Book Club (third Friday of every month) and/or the Evening Book Club (Thursdays) – you can meet people and discuss interesting books.

SAVE Library card annual fees: senior $10 (Adult $14)
Age Requirement for senior category: 65-plus

LIBRARIES – LEDUC

Leduc Public Library
www.library.leduc.ab.ca
#2 Alexandra Park; 986-2637

INFORMATION Enquire about sessions including "Seniors' Computer Basics" and "Seniors' Internet Crash Course."

FREE There is no cost for library cards for residents of Leduc and the County of Leduc.

Wine & Beer Making

The southside *Brew Crew* store at 5718 – 111 Street provides a "Rewards Program" for customers. You get points for dollars spent and then the points can be redeemed for store products. It is free to join. Their telephone number is 431-1944.

The southside *Harvest Brewing Co.* store at 9872 – 63 Avenue (435-2985) has a "frequent buyer program"; after a certain amount of purchases, customers receive a store credit towards future purchases.

Fishing & Hunting

Outdoor sportsman eagerly awaits the arrival of the *Edmonton Boat & Sportsman's Show* at Edmonton Northlands each March. Seniors 65-plus usually get discounted admission and there are many draws to enter and free brochures to bring home, as well as many displays to enjoy while you're at the show.

FREE Annual provincial fishing licenses are free to Albertans, aged 65-plus.

Woodworking

Woodworkers eagerly await the arrival of the *Edmonton Woodworking Show and Sale* each October. Seniors 65-plus usually get discounted admission and there are many draws to enter and free brochures to bring home, plus many displays to enjoy while you're at the show.

Railroad Enthusiasts

If railroads and the history of the railway are your area of interest, you will want to look into joining the *Alberta Pioneer Railway Association* (if you haven't already). This group oversees the Alberta Railway Museum, located west of Fort Saskatchewan. Senior membership is $20 annually (Adult membership is $30 annually). You can learn more about this association on its website, www.railwaymuseum.ab.ca, or you can phone them by calling 472-6229.

History and Family Genealogy

If you are interested in history, particularly Edmonton history, be sure to check with *Edmonton Transit* about their Historic Bus Tours which run from late July to mid-August (Tuesdays, Thursdays and Saturdays). There is informative commentary offered on the tours and the cost is certainly affordable at $4 per person!

There are excellent resources in the *Heritage Room* at the Stanley Milner Library. The *Provincial Archives of Alberta* at 8555 Roper Road (427-1750) is a wonderful research facility with books on Alberta history, microfilms, maps and collections from many Alberta sources such as churches and associations. There is also a splendid photo collection. It is free to do research here and all you have to do is register to receive a "user" card, but you have to pay for photocopies.

You can get free daily or weekly newsletters with valuable family genealogy information and tips by subscribing on-line to *The Ancestry Daily News*. Go to the website www.ancestry.com and follow instruction on how to have this emailed to you.

Annual membership to the *Alberta Genealogical Society,* is $35 for 65-plus (Adult $40). Included in your membership is one branch membership (e.g. Edmonton Branch). The society has great resources including books and microfilm. They are located in the Prince of Wales Armouries in Edmonton (telephone 424-4429).

Birding

If you are a birding enthusiast, you have an opportunity to speak to a naturalist from the *John Janzen Nature Centre* in Edmonton every Monday and Friday from 9 a.m. to noon; this naturalist is available to answer your nature questions including what kind of foods birds love most in winter and what the name of the new bird at your feeder is. The telephone number is 496-2910. There is no charge to speak to a naturalist.

Wildbird General Store
4712 – 99 Street in Edmonton; 439-7333
SAVE Senior customers get a discount on bird seed purchases, always.
Age Requirement: 65-plus

Square Dancing

If you like to square dance, round dance or clog, check with the *Square Dance Association of Edmonton & District!* It's affordable to join and it can put you in touch with many groups in various areas of Edmonton and surrounding communities that dance together regularly. You can call the association at 496-9136.

Chapter 6

Money Matters

Banks and Credit Unions

All the major banks and credit unions have excellent offerings in bank accounts designed especially for senior customers.

In most cases, you need to formally apply for these accounts by visiting your branch in person when you reach the required age – you are *not enrolled automatically* even if you've been a customer for many years. If you are a new customer at a bank, ensure you ask about specific senior accounts if you are of qualifying age.

Listed here are financial institutions in Edmonton and area, and the accounts they offer for senior citizens, plus the age you need to be to benefit from these accounts.

You will need to enquire directly about specifics, but advantages provided by accounts for senior citizens may include: no monthly fee; discount on a safety deposit box; no bank charges to obtain traveller's cheques or money orders; and a certain number of free debit transactions per month.

ATB Financial
www.atb.com

General enquiries: 1-888-330-9282 Toll Free
They offer the *ATB Financial Senior Plan* (59-plus). There are 18 branches in Edmonton, two branches in the communities of Sherwood Park and St. Albert, and one branch in

each of the communities of Spruce Grove, Stony Plain and Leduc.

Bank of Montreal
www.bmo.com
> General enquiries: 1-800-555-3000 Toll Free
> They offer the *Senior Special Discount Program* (60-plus).
> There are 23 branches in Edmonton, three branches in Sherwood Park, two branches in St. Albert, one branch in Spruce Grove and two branches in Leduc.

INFORMATION Bank of Montreal is an Air Miles sponsor and some banking products earn air miles; you will need to enquire about specifics.

Canadian Western Bank
www.cwbank.com
> General enquiries: 423-8888
> They offer the *Gold Leaf PLUS Package* (57-plus).
> There are five Canadian Western Bank branches located in Edmonton.

Capital City Savings Credit Union
www.capitalcitysavings.ca
> General enquiries: 496-2000
> They offer the *Heritage Account* (59-plus, or have been a member with Capital City Savings for 25 years or more and have reached the age of 50). There are 18 branches in Edmonton and one branch in each of the communities of Sherwood Park, St. Albert, Spruce Grove, Stony Plain and Leduc.

Canadian Imperial Bank of Commerce (CIBC)
www.cibc.com
> General enquiries: 429-7744

INFORMATION CIBC provides statements in large print or in Braille if requested.
> They offer the *CIBC For Seniors Advantage Account* (60-plus). There are 16 branches in Edmonton, two in

Sherwood Park and one in each of the communities of
Spruce Grove, Stony Plain and Leduc.

Royal Bank
www.rbcroyalbank.com
General enquiries: 1-800-ROYAL11 (1-800-769-2511) Toll
Free
They offer the *Seniors' Rebate Program* (60-plus). There are
19 branches in Edmonton, and one branch in each of the
communities of Sherwood Park, St. Albert, Spruce Grove
and Leduc.

Scotia Bank
www.scotiabank.com
General enquiries: 448-7600
They offer the *Scotia Plus Program* (59-plus). There are 17
branches in Edmonton, two branches in both of the communities of Sherwood Park and St. Albert, and one branch
in both the communities of Spruce Grove and Leduc.

TD Canada Trust
www.tdcanadatrust.com
General enquiries: 1-866-222-3456 Toll Free
They offer *"Plan 60"* (60-plus). There are 27 branches in
Edmonton, two branches in Sherwood Park and one branch
in each of the communities of Spruce Grove and Leduc.

Income Tax Preparation

H & R Block
www.hrblock.ca
Edmonton Main District Office: 488-2100
INFORMATION This well-known income tax preparation company has many locations in Edmonton and area. The
district office is open year round, and offices in shopping
strip malls and kiosks in major malls are open during tax
season.
SAVE H & R Block provides senior customers(65-plus) with a 10
per cent discount on tax preparation.

Chapter 7

Lifelong Learning

*"Wisdom is not a product of schooling but of the
lifelong attempt to acquire it."*

Albert Einstein (1879-1955)

If you have a thirst for lifelong learning, today's continuing education centres, colleges and universities are willing and able to meet that need. There are some terrific opportunities and monetary savings for seniors. If you become a member of a seniors' club, there are often great general interest courses you can register in.

Depending on your stage in life, you may very well be still working in your career and looking to expand your knowledge or skills. Or you may be looking for a career change and need new skills. If you are retired, perhaps you would enjoy courses that could expand your knowledge of computers or theology. How about a general interest course in scrapbooking or furniture refinishing, gardening or photography? If you've always wanted to learn to speak another language, this may very well be the perfect time in your life to do just that!

At some institutions, there are opportunities to "audit" credit courses that are normally part of a degree or diploma program. The University of Alberta allows auditing, as do Vanguard Bible College and NAIT, for example. The cost for auditing a course, which means that you don't hand in assignments or write exams, is significantly less than for taking a course for credit (generally a 50 per cent discount on the course fee).

Specifically for Senior Lifelong Learners

Edmonton Lifelong Learners Association (ELLA)/University of Alberta
www3.extension.ualberta.ca
>Telephone: 492-5055
>Classes are held in the Education Building at 87 Avenue and 112/114 Street.

>EXCELLENT VALUE Annually, ELLA hosts a three-week Spring Session at the University of Alberta that offers non-credit courses in liberal arts, fine arts, science and the humanities as well as those that emphasize physical and mental well-being. The Spring Session fee is $185 per person (for as many courses as you can fit into your timetable!). You must also purchase an annual ELLA membership at $20 per person to participate.
>Age Requirement: 50-plus

Minerva Senior Studies Institute/Grant MacEwan College
www.macewan.ca/minerva
>Classes are held at the Grant MacEwan downtown campus as well as at other locations, including Strathcona Place Centre and Central Lions Senior Centre; 487-5082.

>EXCELLENT VALUE A variety of classes from writing to computing and many others are held from September to April. Enquire about their *"Walk-About Series"* and their *"Presentation Series."*
>Age Requirement: 50-plus

Educational Institutions Offering Senior Student Fee Reductions
>The following educational institutions offer discounted course fees to seniors students:

Athabasca University
www.athabascau.ca

A distance education and on-line university; 421-8700

INFORMATION Athabasca programs enable you to study at your own pace at home. Anyone is eligible for admission.

SAVE Seniors (Canadian citizens) are offered a reduction in course registration fees. Seniors pay the full learning resources fee portion of a registration but are given a reduction of one-half the tuition registration fee. They are also given a reduction of one-half of the course extension fees. Application fees and any services fees must be paid in full. Age Requirement: 65-plus

Edmonton Public Schools Metro College

Campus downtown at 10135 – 109 Street plus other classroom locations, including the Centre for Education and schools in the Edmonton Public Schools system; 428-1111.

INFORMATION The Computer Internet Learning Centre of Metro College offers specialized courses for seniors (prices reflect a discounted rate); call 917-5053.

SAVE Senior students receive a 10 per cent discount on all continuing education programs offered. Age Requirement: 55-plus

Newman Theological College

www.newman.edu

Campus at 15611 St. Albert Trail; 447-2993

SAVE Senior tuition $220 per on-campus course and $265 per distance education course (Adults $447/$530). All students must pay a Student Association fee of $15 per semester. Age Requirement: 65-plus

Chapter 8

Playing "Tourist" in Edmonton & Area

Here in Edmonton and area, there are many cultural, historical and other attractions and events to enjoy. Sometimes people have the impression that these attractions are only for tourists. They couldn't be more wrong!

Why not "play tourist" by taking in some of these attractions and events? For seniors, the best time to do this, of course, is off-season rather than in July or August or at holiday time in December, as many families with children visit these local attractions at those times. Some of these attractions, notably the outdoor ones, are only open for the mid-May to early-September period. So for seniors, May and June, as well as September, would be perfect months to head out.

Remember that many communities within a day's drive of Edmonton not only have wonderful museums and attractions, but fairs, parades, agricultural events and rodeos as well. Parades are always free to watch and many events in these outlying communities are free to attend or very affordable. Travel Alberta or visitor centres in the communities you plan to visit are great resources for information.

Why not experience something really unique in terms of a summer or early autumn day trip? Call the Alberta Farm Fresh Producers Association for their current brochure *Come To Our Farms... Your Guide to Alberta Farm Fresh Products* (Toll Free 1-800-661-2642 or check their website at www.albertafarmfresh.com). In the brochure, you'll find listings of farms in Edmonton and area where you can visit and purchase fruits, vegetables, protein foods and specialty items. Some of the farms are "U-Pick" operations and the brochure outlines details.

Here's a comprehensive list of attractions and activities that offer wonderful discounts to seniors. Admission to some of these is free. These are all close-by – no more than a day's drive there and back.

For free information on attractions and activities in the Edmonton area, stop by the *Gateway Park Visitor Information Centre* (2404 Gateway Boulevard) or call 496-8400. *Travel Alberta* can provide great information for all communities within the Edmonton vicinity and you can visit their website at www.travelalberta.com. Or, give them a call at 1-800-ALBERTA (1-800-252-3782).

Are you an Alberta Motor Association member? There are a number of area attractions such as *The Fort Saskatchewan Museum* and *Rutherford House,* among others, that participate in the "Show Your Card and Save Program." Refer to the AMA program booklet for a complete list.

EDMONTON

Art Galleries

Alberta Craft Council Art Gallery
www.albertacraft.ab.ca
> 10186 – 106 Street; 488-5900

INFORMATION This gallery showcases exhibitions of contemporary and heritage craft arts, promoting craft artisans from Alberta. Open year round.

FREE Admission is free.

Art Gallery of Alberta (formerly Edmonton Art Gallery)
www.edmontonartgallery.com
> 99 Street and 102 A. Avenue; 422-6223

INFORMATION A permanent collection of over 5,000 works of art plus travelling exhibitions are featured. There is also a free *"Art for Lunch"* Program and free lectures offered in the *"A Visit With the Artist"* series. Open year round (closed Mondays).

SAVE Seniors can save on annual memberships: Senior $30 and Senior Family $45 (Adult $50 and Family $60). There are also senior savings on single admissions: Senior $7 (Adult $10).
Age Requirement: 65-plus

Art Walks/Drives

Art & Design In Public Places Program
Downtown Core; 424-4085 (Edmonton Downtown Business Association)

INFORMATION Varied works of art and design dot the downtown core as part of this program. These are the 13 works installed through the program:

- *Aurora's Dance* (Four-block sculptural fence inspired by the Northern Lights at 104 Street – north of Jasper Avenue and 102 Street – south of Jasper Avenue);
- *Return 2001* (20-foot tower of 390 intertwining rings at 100A Street and Jasper Avenue);
- *Recycles* (Five stationary bicycles operated by peddling and topped with poles and whirlgigs at Jasper Avenue and 105 Street);
- *Sway* (Ceramic tile mosaic mural made up of some 12,000 pieces on the east wall of 10216 – 106 Street);
- *No. 23* (30-foot-high aluminum and steel pipes on the southeast corner of 109 Street and Jasper Avenue);
- *A Walk Through the Universe* (Aerosol graffitti mural at 95 Street and 105 Avenue);
- *Moseyeics* (Modular mural of one hundred and fifty 16' by 16' paintings of the eye at 97 Street and 103 Avenue);
- *Clouds* (25 giant stainless steel clouds on the north parkade wall at 102 Street facing Jasper Avenue);
- *Keep Moving* (1,200-square-foot mural creating a representation of the uses past and present of the Ribbon of Steel railway corridor, on the east and west walls of the 99 Avenue and 110 Street overpass);

- *All Out* (800-square-foot mural celebration the City of Edmonton's Emergency Response Department's 100-year history on the south wall of Firestation #1 at 96 Street and 103 Avenue);
- *Catching Neutrinos* (Edmonton Journal narrative sculptural installation at the northwest corner of Churchill Square in the Indigenous Gardens);
- *Lodge* (TELUS entryway sculptural installation at the southwest corner of Churchill Square); and
- *Light Venturi* (EPCOR water feature sculptural installation in Churchill Square).

FREE These artworks can be viewed for free.

124th Street Gallery Walks
www.gallery-walk.com
        488-0928
FREE The 124th Street Gallery Walks are free events, designed to promote both arts and artists of merit, focusing on work by Canadian artists. There are nine member galleries within a nine-block walking distance. Gallery walks are held each spring, fall and winter.
        Age Requirement: Anyone

Museums

Alberta Aviation Museum
        11410 Kingsway Avenue; 451-1175
INFORMATION This museum has 27 historical aircrafts on display, other exhibits and an active restoration area. Open daily year round except Christmas and New Year's Day.
SAVE Senior admission $5 (Adult $7).
        Age Requirement: 60-plus

Edmonton Public Schools Archives and Museum
        McKay Avenue School at 10425 – 99 Avenue; 422-1970
        If you attended an Edmonton public school during your grade one to grade 12 school years, this museum will surely "bring back the memories!"

INFORMATION The archives and museum is within the beautiful historic McKay Avenue School. See uniforms, textbooks, equipment and photographs of students from the early years of the Edmonton Public School system. Open year round but call ahead for specific days and hours.
AFFORDABLE Admission by donation.

John Walter Museum
www.edmonton.ca/johnwalter
10661 – 91A Avenue on the south bank of the North Saskatchewan River; 496-8787
INFORMATION This museum is comprised of the three original homes of John Walter, one of Edmonton's first entrepreneurs. Open eleven months per year (closed in January).
FREE Admission is free but donations are welcomed.
Age Requirement: Anyone

Loyal Edmonton Regiment Military Museum
www.lermuseum.org
Prince of Wales Armouries at 10440 – 108 Avenue; 421-9943
INFORMATION A military museum featuring memorabilia of the Loyal Edmonton Regiment plus other displays connected with the Canadian military.
FREE Admission is free but donations are welcomed.

Royal Alberta Museum (formerly The Provincial Museum of Alberta)
www.royalalbertamuseum.ca
12845 – 102 Avenue; 453-9100
INFORMATION Permanent displays on Alberta's history and geography and special travelling exhibits. Open year round. This facility is wheelchair accessible.
SAVE The "Annual Mammoth Pass" is available to seniors for $30 per year (Adult $35) and there is a grandparent category for two seniors and two children for $60 annually. Single admission Senior $8 (Adult $10).
INFORMATION "Annual Mammoth Pass" holders receive copies of the *Mammoth Tracks Newsletter,* 10 per cent off in the

Museum Shop, a 10 per cent discount in the Museum Cafe, advance notice of special events and programs and a 50 per cent discount on admission at provincially-owned Historic Sites and Museums.
Age Requirement: 65-plus

Attractions

Alberta Legislature Building
www.assembly.ab.ca
> 10800 – 97 Street; 427-7362 (Visitor Services)

INFORMATION Legislature Building Tours begin at the Interpretive Centre located in the pedway. Tours run daily. Closed Christmas Day, New Year's Day and Good Friday. Wheelchair accessible.

FREE There is no cost to go on a tour of the Alberta Legislature Building.

Edmonton Queen Riverboat
www.edmontonqueen.com
> Rafter's Landing, on the south bank of the river by the Low Level Bridge; 424-2628

SAVE Discounts to seniors on the following packages: Thursday through Saturday – cruise only package Senior $12.50 (Adult $15.95) and cruise dinner package Senior $39 (Adult $46.95). On Sundays, senior pricing is at three levels: brunch cruise is Senior $38.50 (Adult $41.95), family time cruise is Senior $10 (Adult $12.95) and dinner cruise is Senior $39 (Adult $46.95).

INFORMATION The Edmonton Queen cruising season is mid-May to late September. There are no trips on Mondays, Tuesdays and Wednesdays.
Age Requirement: 60-plus

John Janzen Nature Centre
www.edmonton.ca/johnjanzen
> Beside Fort Edmonton Park; 496-8787

INFORMATION A perfect place to take your grandchildren or greatgrandchildren to! Special events and programs are regularly featured. Open year round.

SAVE Senior annual pass $4.25 (Adult $5) and Senior single admission $1.50 (Adult $1.75).
Age Requirement: 65-plus

Muttart Conservatory
www.edmonton.ca/muttart
9626 – 96 A Street; 496-8787

INFORMATION Four glass pyramids nestled in Edmonton's river valley, showcasing the flora and fauna of various regions. There are changing shows in the Show Pyramid and other special events. Open year round.

SAVE Senior "Marigold" Annual Pass $22.75 (Adult $28.00) and Senior single admission $6.50 (Adult $7.50).

INFORMATION A "Marigold" Annual Pass offers unlimited admission during regular public hours for a full year, free admission at over 150 botanic gardens across North America and the Muttart Thymes Newsletter plus special event mailings.
Age Requirement: 65-plus

Valley Zoo
www.edmonton.ca/valleyzoo
87 Avenue and 133 Street; 496-8787

INFORMATION Open year round with many special events on weekends.

SAVE Annual Pass Senior $20 and Annual Pass with Rides Senior $52.75 (Adult Annual Pass $29.50 and Adult Annual Pass with Rides $61.70). Single admissions: Summer (May 8 to October 10 each year) Senior $5.50 (Adult $7.50); Winter (October 11 to May 6 each year) senior $4.25 (Adult $5.50). You can also enquire about purchasing the daily "Grandparents' Pass."

INFORMATION A Valley Zoo Annual Pass offers unlimited admission during regular public hours for a full year, free admis-

sion to over 100 zoos across North America, a copy of the *Wild Times Magazine* plus mail-outs and newsletters.
Age Requirement: 65-plus

West Edmonton Mall
www.westedmall.com
170 Street and 87 Avenue; 444-5200
SAVE *Galaxyland* Indoor Amusement Park Day Pass: Senior $19.95 (Adult $26.95). Note that there is also a daily discount for the last three hours before closing (for anyone) at $16.95 per person.
SAVE *World Waterpark* Day Pass: Senior $19.95 (Adult $26.95).
SAVE *Professor WEM's Adventure Golf*: Senior $5.95 per game (Adult $7.95 per game).
Age Requirement: 55-plus for senior pricing at all three attractions.

Historical Attractions

Fort Edmonton Park
www.fortedmontonpark.com
Corner of Fox Drive and Whitemud Drive; 496-8787
INFORMATION A living museum showcasing Edmonton in its early days; there are costumed intrepreters throughout the park. Admission includes a steam train ride. Open mid-May to late September and over the Christmas season.
SAVE Annual pass: Senior $17.25 (Adult $22.50). Single admission Senior $7.00 (Adult $9.25). The daily "Grandparents' Pass" costs $29.50 and includes two senior admissions and four child admissions. If you are visiting in September, there are wagon rides and seniors ride for $5.50 per person (Adult $7.35).
Age Requirement: 65-plus

Government House Tours
www.albertaheritage.net
Located on the grounds of the Royal Alberta Museum; 427-2281

INFORMATION Between 1913 and 1938 this mansion served as the official residence of Alberta's lieutenant governors. It was also a convalescent hospital for wounded veterans in World War II. Tours are held each Sunday between 1 to 4 p.m. Closed from mid-December to the end of January. The house is wheelchair accessible.

FREE There is no charge for these tours.

Rutherford House
www.cd.gov.ab.ca and click on "Enjoying Alberta"
11153 Saskatchewan Drive; 427-3995

INFORMATION Costumed intrepreters bring life in 1915 alive at Rutherford House! This restored Edwardian mansion was the home of Alberta's first premier, Alexander Cameron Rutherford. Special events are held on weekends. Open year round (in summer, open daily, and winter, Tuesday through Sunday).

SAVE Senior admission $2 (Adult $3)

Historical Walking Tours

Historical Walking Tours of Downtown Edmonton
496-6123 (City of Edmonton, Planning & Development Department)

INFORMATION There are four tours of downtown Edmonton and they can be followed individually or in sequence. A free booklet outlining these tours is available; it gives excellent background on the buildings along the tour routes. To obtain a copy, call the telephone number above. The brochure is also available from the Downtown Business Association, located at 10121 Jasper Avenue, between 9 a.m. and 5 p.m. Monday through Thursday and 9 a.m. to 4 p.m. on Fridays.

- *Tour I:* Heritage Trail
- *Tour II:* Jasper West and Warehouse District
- *Tour III:* Downtown and Rice Howard Way
- *Tour IV:* Jasper East

FREE The tours are self-directed, following the routes in the brochure (starting points for each walking tour are clearly indicated).

Science Centre

TELUS World of Science (formerly Odyssium)
www.odyssium.com
> 11211 – 142 Street; 451-3344

INFORMATION A science centre featuring six exhibit galleries
and an observatory. There are also two theatres (one an
IMAX) in the centre.

SAVE Annual memberships – Type A: Grandparent Membership
(2 grandparents and up to four children or youth) $100
(Family Membership $115); Type B: Senior $40 (Adult
$50). Note that annual membership benefits include 20
per cent discounts in the gift shop, 10 per cent discounts
in the cafe and theatre concessions, plus discounted pricing on IMAX Theatre tickets. Single admission to galleries
and observatory: Senior $8.95 (Adult $9.95). Combination
admission to galleries and one IMAX film same day: senior
$13.50 (Adult $15.95).

Age Requirement for senior category of Type A and B memberships, single admissions and combination admissions:
65-plus

SHERWOOD PARK

Museum

Strathcona County Museum
> 913 Ash Street; 467-8189

INFORMATION Strathcona County's natural and human history
is showcased at this museum. Open Monday to Friday, year
round.

AFFORDABLE Admission is $3 for everyone.

Attraction

Elk Island National Park
> 20 minutes east of Sherwood Park on Highway 16
> (Yellowhead); 992-2950

INFORMATION How fortunate we are to have a national park just
just a short drive east of Edmonton! This beautiful forested

sanctuary boasts over 250 species of birds, including the threatened trumpeter swan, and is home to moose, elk, beaver, and bison. There are self-guided trails, a floating boardwalk and picnic areas. The park itself is open year-round but some facilities are only open in the summer-time. The Friends of Elk Island Society organizes monthly guided hikes in Elk Island Park; check their website at www.elkisland.ca for further information.

SAVE Daily entry Senior $5 (Adult $6).
Age Requirement: 65-plus

Historical Walking Tour

Sherwood Park Heritage Mile

INFORMATION You can to obtain a free brochure outlining in-formation about Sherwood Park's Heritage Mile from the Sherwood Park and District Chamber of Commerce of-fice (464-0801). You can walk the route along groomed trails or drive between the buildings. Featured are the Ottewell Centre (1916), Salisbury United Church (1915), and Smeltzer House (1920) and there is information about the Smyth Farm (1911) in the Broadmoor Business Centre. Also take in Monument Park at the corner of Broadmoor Boulevard and Athabasan Avenue.

FREE Visiting points on the Heritage Mile is free.

Walking Tour

FREE Broadmoor Park in the centre of Sherwood Park has paved lakeside walking trails. Canada Geese make their home here!

ST. ALBERT

Art Gallery

Profiles Art Gallery

www.stalbert.ca
19 Perron Street, 460-4310

INFORMATION Open year round.

AFFORDABLE Admission by donation.
Age Requirement: Anyone

Museum

Musée Heritage Museum
5 St. Anne Street in St. Albert Place; 459-1528
INFORMATION Features exhibits on the history of St. Albert and
area, plus travelling exhibits. Open year round.
FREE Admission is free, but a $2 donation per person would be
greatly appreciated.
Age Requirement: Anyone

Historical Attraction

Father Lacombe Chapel
www.cd.gov.ab.ca click on "Enjoying Alberta" and "Musems and
Historical Sites"
St. Vital Avenue just off St. Albert Trail; 459-7663
INFORMATION Interpretive guided tours are provided for the
chapel and historic mission. Note that tours are available
in both English and French. Open mid-May to Labour Day.
SAVE Senior admission $1.50 (Adult $2)
Age Requirement: "Senior" (see page 3)

Historical Walking Tour

Morninville Historical Walking Tour
FREE Just north of St. Albert is the Town of Morvinville. A self-
guided Historic Morinville Walking Tour takes in the stun-
ning St. Jean Baptiste Catholic Church on Main Street and
provides a look at the exteriors of historic homes in the
townsite. Call the town office at 939-7702 for further information.

SPRUCE GROVE

Art Gallery

Little Church Gallery
455 King Street, 962-0664

INFORMATION A volunteer artist-run society presenting the
works of local artists (Allied Arts Council). The gallery is
open Tuesday through Sunday from noon to 5 p.m., year
round.
FREE Admission is free.

Walking Tour

Heritage Grove Park
FREE There are 22 kilometres of paved walking trails in the
Spruce Grove parks system. In Heritage Grove Park, you
will enjoy natural woodlands and five "outdoor class-
rooms" which describe the history and the unique eco-sys-
tem in the park. Further information is available from the
City of Spruce Grove (962-2611).

STONY PLAIN

Museum

Pioneer Museum
5120 – 43 Avenue; 963-1234
INFORMATION This museum preserves the agricultural heritage of the Stony Plain area. Open daily from early April
to the end of October, 7 days per week. The museum's tea
house serves well-priced lunches and desserts to visitors on
Fridays and Saturdays.
AFFORDABLE Admission for everyone is $2 per person.
Age Requirement: Anyone

Historical attraction

Stony Plain Multicultural Heritage Centre
5411 – 51 Street; 963-2777
INFORMATION Enjoy seeing the General Store, art work in the
gallery and the exhibit dedicated to Mrs. Cornelia Wood.
The Heritage Kitchen serves light lunches and desserts and
coffee at reasonable prices. The centre is open year round
except the week between Christmas and New Year's Day.
AFFORDABLE Admission is by donation.

Historical walking tour:

FREE Since 1990, the town of Stony Plain has been recreating local history through its murals program. There are currently 21 life-size outdoor murals and one statue. You can pay to take a guided tour of the murals on foot or by vehicle by contacting the Multicultural Heritage Centre at 963-2777. You can preview the murals by checking the Town of Stony Plain website at www.stonyplain.com.

LEDUC

Museum

Dr. Woods House Museum
4801 – 48 Avenue; 986-1517

INFORMATION This museum was once the home of Dr. Robert Woods, who practised medicine in Leduc during the 1920s. His medical office was in this home.

AFFORDABLE Admission by donation.

Walking Tour

Leduc Multi Trails System

FREE Leduc's Multi Trails System include over 33 kilometres of pathways. You can access a map of it on the City of Leduc website at www.city.leduc.ab.ca or get further information by calling 980-7177.

DEVON

Attraction

Devonian Botanic Garden
www.devonian.ualberta.ca
5 kilometres north of Devon on Highway #60; 987-3054

INFORMATION This is a regional centre for horticultural and environmental collections of living plants and fungi. Featured are a Japanese garden, floral gardens and collections of alpine and native plants. Open daily from late April to Thanksgiving, and weekends from Thanksgiving to early December.

SAVE Daily admission: Senior $8 (Adult $10). From July 2 to
     August 27, if you arrive after 6 p.m., you pay half-price
     (anyone).
     Age Requirement: 65-plus for senior pricing

Historical Attraction

Canadian Petroleum Interpretive Centre
www.c-pic.org
     2 km south of Devon on Hwy 60; 987-4323
INFORMATION This centre salutes the determination and success
     of the Alberta oil patch with indoor and outdoor exhibits
     related to the Leduc #1 oil well, where oil was struck in
     1947. Open year round.
SAVE Admission senior $4 (Adult $5)
     Age Requirement: 65-plus

FORT SASKATCHEWAN

Museums

Alberta Railway Museum
www.railwaymuseum.ab.ca
     West of Fort Saskatchewan at 24215 – 34 Street
     (Edmonton); 472-6229
INFORMATION This museum houses a collection of equipment
     and buildings all relating to the railroad, notably Canadian
     National Railways and Northern Alberta Railways locomo-
     tives and cars. During the summer, speeder cars run daily,
     offering passenger rides. On holiday weekends, there is pas-
     senger service with locomotives available. Open Victoria
     Day to Labour Day, daily. Guided and self-guided tours are
     offered.
SAVE Senior admission $2.50 (Adult $4).
     Age Requirement: "Senior" (see page 3)

Fort Saskatchewan Museum and Historic Site
     10104 – 101 Street; 998-1750
INFORMATION This museum operated by the Fort Saskatchewan
     Historical Society preserves the history and heritage of the

town. It is housed in the old courthouse, built in 1909.
Featured is an artifact collection that depicts the history
of the Northwest Mounted Police presence in the Fort
Saskatchewan area. In July and August, open daily. From
September to June, reduced hours daily; closed for the
Christmas, New Year and Easter holidays, and closed week-
ends in January, February and March.

AFFORDABLE Admission per senior is $3 (Adults $4).
Age Requirement: "Senior" (see page 3)

Walking Tour

Fort Saskatchewan Walking Trails

FREE There are 29 kilometres of paved pathways to enjoy – perfect if you like to walk! You can obtain further information
from the Fort Saskatchewan Visitor Information Centre at
998-1783.

KALYNA COUNTRY

Kalyna Country Ecomuseum/Lamont County Region
www.kalynacountry.ab.ca
To obtain a Visitor's Guide: 1-800-452-5962

INFORMATION Just 50 kilometres northeast of Edmonton is a
huge area of rich farmland and scenic countryside. There is
lots to see and do in this area – all within a day's drive of
the Edmonton area.

Museum

Basilian Fathers' Museum & Monastery
www.basilianmuseum.org
5335 Sawchuk Street in Mundare; (780) 764-3887

INFORMATION This museum showcases the history of Ukrainian
settlement and the Basilian Fathers Mission in Canada.
Open year round from Monday to Friday, and also on
weekends in the summer.

AFFORDABLE Admission by donation.

Attractions

Mallard Sculpture

FREE The world's largest mallard sculpture, with a 28-foot wing-span, can be viewed along with a historic grain elevator in the Village of Andrew.

Ukrainian Sausage Sculpture

FREE See the world's largest Ukrainian sausage in Mundare – a town famous for its sausage making. You can also visit the Mundare Sausage House in town to bring Ukrainian sausage home!

Historical attractions

Church Capital of North America

INFORMATION Lamont County is Church Capital of North America with 47 churches that you can drive around and see. You can purchase a booklet for $2 from several outlets in the county or download if from www.countylamont.ab.ca. One of the historic monuments in this area is the Grotto of Our Lady of Lourdes (located at the junction of Highways 831 and 45).

Health History Mural

FREE In Lamont, a 66-foot-long painted mural in the Lamont Health Care Centre depicts 90 years of health history in the area.

Remembrance Day Mural

FREE The community of Chipman has a very unique Remembrance Day Mural, which is painted on the side of the Seniors' Drop-In Centre. The mural depicts the faces of village sons and daughters who served during the two world wars.

Ukrainian Cultural Heritage Village

www.cd.gov.ab.ca and click on "Enjoying Alberta" and "Museums and Historical Sites"

Highway 16 (Yellowhead) 1/2 hour east of Sherwood Park; (780) 662-3640

INFORMATION This heritage village museum has over 30 historic buildings restored to their original condition, including three Eastern Byzantine Rite churches. Costumed role players portray original characters from 1892 to 1930. Many special events are held on weekends throughout the summer. Open daily from the May Long Weekend to Labour Day.

SAVE Admission Senior $7 (Adult $8)
Age Requirement: 65-plus

Victoria Settlement

www.cd.gov.ab.ca and click on "Enjoying Alberta" and "Museums and Historical Sites"

10 kilometres south of Smoky Lake on secondary highway #855; (780) 656-2333

INFORMATION In 1892 Reverend George McDougall founded Victoria Settlement on the bank of the North Saskatchewan as a Methodist mission. The Hudson's Bay Company then established Fort Victoria as a trading post in 1894. The original Clerk's Quarters of the fort and a Methodist Church are showcased and there are costumed interpreters on site. Open May 15 to Labour Day, daily.

SAVE Senior admission $1.50 (Adult $2).
Age Requirement: 65-plus

VEGREVILLE

Museum

Vegreville Regional Museum

One kilometre east of Vegreville on Highway 16A; (780) 632-7560

INFORMATION Showcases Vegreville's history dating back to 1894. Special events in the summertime include heritage demonstrations, classic car shows and farm machinery displays. Open year round with reduced hours from September to May.

AFFORDABLE Admission by donation.

Attractions

Pysanka Monument

FREE See the world's largest pysanka (Ukrainian Easter egg) located in the Elks/Kinsmen Park. This huge monument celebrates the Ukrainian heritage of the Vegreville area and weighs 3,000 pounds. It contains 54 star patterns, 1,108 equilateral triangles, 3,512 visible facets, 6,978 nuts and bolts and 177 internal struts and stands 31 feet high.

Highway 16A Shrine

FREE *Our Lady of the Highway Shrine* is located just east of Vegreville on Highway 16 A. The shrine exists to protect and direct people on their voyages. It is seven feet high and was sculpted in Italy from Carrara marble.

Historical attraction

Vegreville Historical Mural

FREE See the Vegreville Rotary Club's mural depicting the community's history and cultures. It is located in the downtown Rendezvous Park.

Historical walking tour

Alberta Main Street Tour

www.touralbertamainstreets.ca

FREE Enjoy learning the history of main street Vegreville on the "Tour Alberta Main Streets" website. Then, plan to spend a day in Vegreville touring and seeing historical buildings including the Dobbins Block (1913), Shirley's Beauty Salon (1940s-era) and the Capitol Theatre (1950s-era), plus historic plaques.

CAMROSE

Museum

Camrose & District Centennial Museum
www.camrose.com
> 46 Avenue and 53 Street; (780) 672-3298

INFORMATION One main building and nine outside buildings form this museum which is home to thousands of artifacts. Open Victoria Day to Labour Day but closed Mondays.

AFFORDABLE Admission by donation.

Walking Tour

Mirror Lake Park
FREE There is a 2.2-kilometre loop (about a 30-minute walk) on a trail system around Mirror Lake. A brick wall sculpture depicts the plant and wildlife in the area. In summertime, swans grace the lake. The trail is paved and wheelchair-friendly!

Historical Walking Tour

Alberta Main Street Tour
www.touralbertamainstreets.ca
FREE Enjoy learning about the history of Camrose on the "Tour Alberta Main Streets" website. Then, plan to spend a day in Camrose touring!

WETASKIWIN

Museums

Alberta Central Railway Museum
> Located just outside Wetaskiwin, (780) 352-2257

INFORMATION The rail yard and exhibits tell the story of the work of railroaders, of train travel in Canada and the impact the CPR had on settlement of Western Canada. Visitors can take a ride on a restored 1926 first-class observation-buffet-sleeper. Open May Long Weekend to Labour Day (closed Mondays and Tuesdays).

AFFORDABLE Adult admission is $4 and the train fare for adult is $4 (no specific senior age pricing). They have "Looney Tuesday" admission days several times per season; you only pay $2 admission on those days.

Reynolds-Alberta Museum and Canada's Aviation Hall of Fame
www.cd.gov.ab.ca (click on "Enjoying Alberta")
Located two kilometres west of Wetaskiwin; Toll Free 1-800-661-4726

INFORMATION This museum and hall of fame showcases Alberta's agriculture, transportation and aviation history in buildings and on the land surrounding the museum. Many special events are held throughout the year. Open year round, every day during peak season, closed Mondays during off season).

SAVE Senior daily admission is in two seasonal categories: Senior admission off season (September 6 to May 13) is $5.50 (Adult $6.50); Senior admission peak season (May 14 to September 5) is $7 (Adult $9).
Age Requirement: 65-plus

Wetaskiwin & District Heritage Museum
5007 – 50 Avenue; (780) 352-0227

INFORMATION Three floors of exhibits including a war exhibit, early businesses of the area exhibit, immigration exhibit and one entitled "Women of Aspenland." Guided tours are available. Open year round but closed Mondays in the summertime, and Sundays and Mondays in the off-season.

FREE Admission is free but donations are welcomed.

Walking Tour

Wetaskiwin Walking Tour

FREE If you like walking, there is a wonderful paved trail which includes a stop at the By-The-Lake Park and the Prairie Garden (a demonstrative garden of the variety of crops grown in the area). You can get detailed information from Wetaskiwin Tourism at (780) 352-8003.

Historical Walking Tour

Alberta Main Street Tour
www.touralbertamainstreets.ca

FREE Enjoy learning about Wetaskiwin history on the "Tour
Alberta Main Streets" website. Then, plan to spend a day in
Wetaskiwin touring!

STETTLER

Museum

Stettler Town & Country Museum
6302 – 44 Avenue; (780) 742-4534

INFORMATION This is a historic "village" with eleven buildings
including a church, courthouse and general store. Open
May 1 to September 7 daily.

SAVE Senior admission $2 (Adult $3)
Age Requirement: "Senior" (see page 3)

Attraction

Alberta Railway Excursions
4611 – 47 Avenue; (403) 742-2811

INFORMATION This company offers a range of day trips aboard
a steam or diesel-locomotive powered train. They begin
in Stettler, travel to Big Valley and then return to Stettler.
There are a variety of categories to choose from. Some
trips include meals on-board while others include a meal
in Big Valley, and all trips include on-board entertainment
(music and sometimes train robberies!). Alberta Railway
Excursions run from mid-May to late September and there
are also some special December excursions.

AFFORDABLE Although there is no specific senior pricing on
these excursions, you can choose the "Economy Special to
Big Valley" (buy one ticket at regular fare, get one at half-
price) or the "Senior Special To Big Valley" (every group
that includes at least one senior receives a 10 per cent discount on all fares in the group). Special rates are also available for parties of 20 or more.

Chapter 9

Automotive

A number of automotive and related businesses in Edmonton and area offer discounts to seniors. Some offer savings through coupon offers.

Becoming a member (or renewing your membership) in the Alberta Motor Association provides great "peace of mind" for automobile owners. Although AMA doesn't offer specific senior membership pricing category upon joining, they do offer senior membership pricing on renewals. Memberships are affordable and invaluable. See information on joining or renewing on AMA in this chapter. Information on the AMA "*Show Your Card and Save*" program is detailed in Chapter 11, *Miscellaneous Discounts and Savings*.

AMA members can take advantage of the "*Show Your Card and Save Program*," through which you will get savings at a number of auto, battery, glass and lube shops. Check the guide provided with your AMA membership package.

Are you an Air Miles collector? Listed throughout this chapter are Air Mile sponsors in the automotive and automotive-related product area.

If you want to stay on top of current gas prices, there is a website you can access: www.gasbuddy.com. The home page displays a Canadian map – click on AB and choose the link EdmontonGasPrices.com. The website lists price, station name, area of the city the station is located in and the time the gas price was reported. The information is a live forum for consumers to post local recent low and high gasoline prices – allowing consumers to save money at the pumps.

For those of you with a keen interest in cars, motorbikes and recreational vehicles, the following consumer shows may be of interest. Most consumer shows offer discounted admission to seniors that is $2 to $3 less than adult admission.

- *Edmonton Motorcycle Show* (Edmonton Northlands; January)
- *Edmonton Motorshow* (Edmonton Northlands; February)
- *Edmonton RV Exposition and Sale* (Edmonton Northlands; February)

Proper Maintenance Saves Money

Proper maintenance of your vehicle is very important. That includes things like regular oil changes and anti-freeze checks, along with checking your tire pressure on a regular basis.

Car Pooling and Ride-Sharing Saves Money

Two concepts for saving money on transportation are car-pooling and ride sharing. Both of these have merit and can work within groups of friends who share similar interests and attend the same senior recreation centre, for instance. Gasoline costs can be shared and the reduced wear-and-tear on your vehicle is a savings, too.

Alberta Motor Association Memberships

Alberta Motor Association (AMA)
www.ama.ab.ca

INFORMATION AMA member services include auto emergency road service, vehicle registry, insurance, a travel agency plus access to free maps and tourist guides. Members receive discounts on passport photos. There is a fabulous "*Show Your Card and Save Program*," through which members benefit from many discounts (see further information on this program in Chapter 11 under "Loyalty Programs"). You also receive their magazine, *Westworld*, by mail. With your AMA membership, you can enjoy savings on accommodations, car rentals, restaurants, museums and theme parks in North America and even in other countries. But undoubtedly the biggest benefit of AMA is the "peace of mind" it offers to drivers!

AFFORDABLE When you first join AMA, everyone, regardless of age, pays the same basic rate of $61 per year plus a one-time registration fee of $15. You can choose to enhance your membership to a CAA Plus category or CAA Plus RV category (ask AMA to explain the pricing on these levels to you).

SAVE In your first and subsequent years of renewal, a senior savings of $4 per member is applied to the basic membership. Age Requirement for senior pricing on renewals: 65-plus

Full-Service Car Washes

Owning a car means maintaining it regularly, and exterior washes and interior cleaning are part of that regular maintenance. There are two full-service car wash companies operating in Edmonton and area where they do the vacuuming and interior cleaning for you, along with the outside wash, in their automated car wash/hand dry. All you have to do is pay and drive away! Here are details of savings in this area:

Bubbles Car Wash
www.bubbles.ca

SAVE $5 off all washes at the "Early Bird Special," 8 to 10 a.m., on Mondays, Tuesdays and Wednesdays.

LOCATED IN EDMONTON
- 10212 – 108 Street; 423-5206
- 11828 – 104 Avenue; 448-9274
- 16907 Stony Plain Road; 484-4949
- 10538 – 82 Avenue; 433-1540
- 9330 – 51 Avenue; 430-9884
- 13804 – 127 Street; 456-7474

LOCATED IN SHERWOOD PARK
- 25 Athabascan Avenue; 464-6420

- 40 Green Grove Drive; 460-4401

LOYALTY PROGRAM The Bubbles Points Club is free to join and
you earn points each time you visit. Points can be redeemed
for rewards such as air freshener applications.
Age Requirement: Anyone

Cupid's Car Wash
7303 Gateway Boulevard; 439-5664

SAVE Early Bird Special from 8 to 10 a.m., Monday through
Thursday.

SAVE "Senior Day" is every Wednesday, with savings all day.
Age Requirement: Anyone for Early Bird Specials and 60-
plus for "Senior Day" savings.

Gasoline

There are a number of ways you can save with "cash back
discounts," "rebate books" and "loyalty programs" when you fill
up your vehicle.

As well, on a regular basis, some stations automatically offer
a discount at the pumps off the posted gas price displayed on their
signage. Safeway Gas Bars offer discounts to Safeway Club Card
members.

Canada Flying J Travel Centre (SHELL gasoline)
Yellowhead Hwy. and Broadmoor Boulevard in Sherwood
Park; 416-2035

LOYALTY PROGRAM The Canada Flying J Rewards Club is free to
join. Members automatically receive instant fuel discounts
(gasoline and propane) and can earn higher fuel discounts
through non-fuel purchases at the Flying J Restaurant
(which also provides a senior discount!), the fast food
outlets and the convenience store. Month-to-date non-
fuel purchases will automatically accumulate to increase a
customer's gasoline discounts in the next calendar month.
The *Rewards Club* brochure explains all details.

LOYALTY PROGRAM SHELL gasoline is an Air Miles sponsor, so customers also earn Air Miles on their gasoline purchases when they fill up at Canada Flying J Travel Centre.
Age Requirement: Anyone

DOMO
www.domo.ca

LOYALTY PROGRAM Domo gas stations offer "cash rebates" right at the pump. The type of rebate depends on market conditions. Participating stations also offer a free gift in the DOMO Rewards Program; check at one the stations for information on these rewards.

There are 16 stations in Edmonton and one each in Sherwood Park and St. Albert.

ESSO
www.essoextra.com

LOYALTY PROGRAM ESSO stations offer the ESSO Extra Points Program. You can join the program free at any station or online (or by telephone 1-800-567-3776 Toll Free). Customers earn points on every fill-up and on convenience store purchases. Points can be redeemed "at the station extras" such as car washes, gas or candy or for "online/by phone" extras like gift certificates or movie passes.

There are 31 stations in Edmonton, three in Sherwood Park, two in St. Albert, one in Spruce Grove, two in Stony Plain and one in Leduc.

FAS GAS/FAS GAS PLUS

LOYALTY PROGRAM When you fuel up at participating stations, have the cashier record your fuel purchase on your "litre log." When you reach 21 fills or $150 in combined fuel purchases, receive two per cent cash back. Customers can then start a new "litre log."

INFORMATION Coffee fans, ask for a free Fresh Brew Card. Buy four coffees, get a stamp for each purchase, and the fifth cup of fresh-brewed coffee is free of charge (you can then start another card!).

There are four stations in Edmonton, two in Sherwood Park and one in Spruce Grove.

Hughes Petroleum
www.hughespetroleum.com

LOYALTY PROGRAM A "customer card" (free to obtain at any of the stations or printable off their website) entitles you to save 3.5 cents per litre for gas and diesel (the card must be presented at the time of each purchase).

There are 16 stations in Edmonton, and one in each of the following communities: Sherwood Park, St. Albert, Spruce Grove and Leduc.

Husky/Mohawk
www.huskyenergy.ca

PROMOTION Present your AMA card when buying gas at any Husky or Mohawk service station to earn AMA Dollars. AMA Dollars are stored in your membership account and can be redeemed on your next AMA renewal or on other AMA services. You can earn AMA Dollars on convenience store purchases and car washes (at stations that have them) and at Husky House Restaurants (at stations that have them). Required for participating in this promotion: AMA membership.

There are 39 stations in Edmonton, five in Sherwood Park, five in St. Albert, three in Spruce Grove and two in Leduc.

Petro Canada
www.petro-canada.com

LOYALTY PROGRAM The Petro-Points Program, which is free to join, enables you to earn points on your fuel and convenience-store purchases. You can redeem points for items such as emergency first aid kits, antifreeze and motor oil, or for travel rewards. You can check your Petro-Points balance on-line and also browse through the rewards on-line).

There are 31 stations in Edmonton, three in Sherwood Park, four in St. Albert and one each in the communities of Spruce Grove, Stony Plain and Leduc.

SHELL
www.shell.ca

LOYALTY PROGRAM All SHELL stations are Air Mile Sponsors.

INFORMATION Their website has a link to "Motoring With Shell," which features the Encyclopedia of Motoring, SHELL Motoring Tips, Fuel Saver and Motor Travelling Assistant.

LOYALTY PROGRAM SHELL stations are Air Mile sponsors. Bonus Air Mile promotions are held regularly.

There are 29 stations in Edmonton, two in Sherwood Park and four in St. Albert.

TURBO

LOYALTY PROGRAM The two TURBO gas stations in Edmonton, at 10931 – 156 Street and 12621 Victoria Trail, are Air Mile sponsors.

Automotive Services

If you check the current Edmonton & Area SuperPages Coupons at the front of the yellow page directory, you will find some great savings coupons from companies such as *Alberta Brake Service, Fastech Performance Tire Centres* and *Jeff's Auto Glass*. Be aware and that you will need to present the coupons to take advantage of savings, that these SuperPages Coupons have expiry dates and also that advertisers and their offers can change from year to year.

Here are some companies who offer senior discounts on their services. You will need to talk to them directly about what age you need to be to obtain their senior discount and discuss what your specific requirements are. You will also need to enquire whether the discounts are on labour, on parts, or on both.

Tires/Automotive Repair:

At *Fountain Tire/GOOD YEAR* shops located in and around Edmonton, you can earn Air Miles on your tire purchases and maintenance as well as on repair services, as they are an Air Miles sponsor.

The yellow page advertisement for *Park Mufflers, Radiators, Brakes and Tires* indicates they offer a "senior citizen discount." See section below on "Mufflers and Radiators."

Autobody/Painting:

The yellow page advertisement for *The Auto Spot,* located at 16390 – 109 Avenue in Edmonton, indicates that they offer a seniors' discount on painting and autobody work. Phone 484-6275.

Brakes:

The yellow page advertisement for *Capilano Brake Shop* indicates they offer a 10 per cent seniors' discount. They are located in Edmonton at 9925 – 50 Street. Phone 468-4534.

The yellow page advertisement for *Park Mufflers, Radiators, Brakes and Tires* indicates they offer a "senior citizen discount". See section below on "Mufflers and Radiators."

Mufflers and Radiators:

The yellow page advertisement for *Park Mufflers, Radiators, Brakes and Tires* indicates they offer a "senior citizen discount." Their shop is located at 101 Seneca Road in Sherwood Park; phone 464-7887. Courtesy cars are available.

Oil/Filter Changes:

Econo-Lube

Highway 16 West in Spruce Grove; 962-1117

SAVE Senior customers receive $5 off the cost of an oil change. Age Requirement: "Senior" (see page 3)

LUBE-X

There are quite a number of Lube-X shops in Edmonton and area.

SAVE This chain of oil change shops regularly offers $4 dollars off coupons for drive-through oil changes on your vehicle. Watch for these coupons in coupon books that are delivered to your home.

Age Requirement: Anyone with coupon

Mr. Lube
www.mrlube.com

There are quite a number of Mr. Lube shops in Edmonton and area.

SAVE If you are an AMA member you save, as services by Mr. Lube are discounted as part of the "Show Your Card & Save" Program.

FREE While your oil change is being done, you can enjoy a fresh cup of coffee and the daily newspaper!

INFORMATION Their website has a link called "Mr. Tips" from which you can learn valuable tips on automobile mainte- nance and seasonal tips (about getting your car ready for winter, for instance). Also offered on-line is a link to a maintenance records page where you can keep track of all your maintenance and requirements for your vehicle.

Requirement "Show Your Card & Save" Program discounts: AMA membership

Transmissions:

The yellow page advertisements for the following companies indicate they offer seniors' discounts.

- *A & C Transmission Specialists;* 454-8598
- *Alberta Transmission Service;* 448-1686
- *City Transmissions Ltd.;* 476-4867
- *Mister Transmission;* northside phone 475-9228, southside phone 442-0000 and west end phone 489-3223. Courtesy cars are available.

Towing and Boosting:

The yellow page advertisement for **Custom Auto Carriers** indicates they offer a seniors' discount. For 24-hour towing/ boosting service, call them at 448-7371.

Locked out of your vehicle?

Oops! Locking keys in a car happens to everyone at some time or another. The following companies offer mobile locksmith

service (and offer senior discounts, according to their yellow page advertisements!).
- Ever Ready Locksmiths – 478-1570
- Master Locksmiths Ltd. – 474-9011

Windshields:

At the four *Speedy Glass* locations in Edmonton and their shop in St. Albert, you can earn Air Miles on windshield replacements and repairs, as they are an Air Miles sponsor. If you are an AMA member, you can show your membership card for the specified Speedy Glass discount.

Automobile Insurance

There is much diversity here in terms of what scope of coverage you require, based on the vehicle you drive.

One company that specializes in automobile insurance for seniors is *Grey Power Insurance Brokers* (#102, 14310 – 111 Avenue; 488-5555). This company also has a home insurance division.

Check with your broker (or if you are shopping around for a new broker) on the following possible discounts:
- Discounts for mature drivers (50-plus);
- Installed car alarm systems;
- Claims-free/clear driving record; and
- Experienced driver.

Chapter 10

Pet Stores, Book Stores, Card Shops and Gift Shops

This chapter covers savings at pet stores and pet groomers and also provides you with a comprehensive list of off-leash areas where you can enjoy walking your dog.

Continuing into the chapter, there are also listings of great bookstores which offer senior discounts or loyalty reward programs. Card shops and gift shops are also featured and they too offer some great savings to senior customers.

Pet Stores & Supplies

Evolution of Pets
15105 Stony Plain Road in Edmonton; 484-1303

SAVE This pet store will give senior customers a discount.
Age Requirement: "Senior" (see page 3)

Petcetera
www.petcetera.ca

LOYALTY REWARDS PROGRAM It is free to join the "Petcetera Plus Club"; you can join on-line or at any store. Use your Petcetera Plus card for the lowest price guarantee, participation in the free bag of dog or cat food promotion (buy 10, get a coupon for one free) plus exclusive offers and specials.

INFORMATION Petcetera stores have monthly specials advertised in their flyers.

- 12222 – 137 Avenue; 456-7976
- 2621 – 66 Street; 462-2608
- West Edmonton Mall; 489-3033
  Age Requirement: Anyone

Pet Planet
www.petplanet.ca

SAVE Every Sunday is "Senior Day" and customers receive a 20 per cent discount on certain pet foods, a 10 per cent discount on cat food and litter if bought together and a 10 per cent discount on bulk treats (with purchase of a specified minimum amount).

- 2126 – 109 Street; 439-9565
- 14979 Stony Plain Road; 489-2072
- 9631 – 167 Avenue; 472-3647
- 700 Riverbend Square; 433-7474
- New store opening at Lessard Road and 184 Street
  Age Requirement: 65-plus

PetSmart
www.petsmart.com

LOYALTY REWARDS PROGRAM It's free for any pet owner to join "The Pet Perks Program." Cardholders get special prices on each week's featured items.

INFORMATION Their website has links to "Pet Care Guides" and a "Pet Food Calculator."

- 3289 Calgary Trail; 434-6611
- 9934 – 170 Street; 486-7800
- 13680 – 50 Street; 456-0910
- 13916 – 137 Avenue; 406-0827
  Age Requirement: Anyone

Pookie's Pet Food
306, 101 Granada Boulevard in Sherwood Park; 464-1228

SAVE 15 per cent discount on all purchases, always.

Age Requirement: 65-plus

Wags 'N Wishes Pet Bakery 'N Deli

SAVE Seniors save every day by paying no GST on bakery and deli purchases. This company also does pet grooming under the name Animal Crackers Pet Grooming & Spa (see under "Pet Grooming").

LOCATED IN EDMONTON

- 11208 – 143 Street; 453-3949
- 7338 – 82 Avenue; 468-3949
  Age Requirement: 65-plus

Pet Grooming

Animal Crackers Pet Grooming & Spa

SAVE Seniors save every day by paying no GST on grooming services. This company also has a pet bakery and deli under the name of *Wags 'N Wishes Pet Bakery 'N Deli* (see under "Pet Stores and Supplies").

LOCATED IN EDMONTON

- 11208 – 143 Street; 453-3949
- 7338 – 82 Avenue; 468-3949
  Age Requirement: 65-plus

Companions and Friends

www.companions-and-friends.com
5537 – 97 Street in Edmonton; 489-8844

SAVE On the website of this company (which offers dog and cat grooming), it states "senior discounts available"; you will need to enquire about the qualifying age for the discount. This company also operates a "Doggy Day Care."

The Groomer's Workshop

10050 – 163 Street in Edmonton; 448-5801

INFORMATION This shop offers traditional dog grooming by appointment or drop-in self-groomers can come by anytime (shampoo and towels are part of the self-grooming price). The Groomer's Workshop offers a 10 per cent senior dis-

count. *This unique discount applies to senior dogs* – 10-plus years – not to senior humans!
Age Requirement: Senior dog aged 10-plus years

The Pampered Puppy
10942 – 124 Street; 732-7277

SAVE Seniors receive a 10 per cent discount, every day. Open early morning to late evening.
Age Requirement: 65-plus

Sadie's Pet Stop
5716 – 111 Street; 448-1737

CUSTOMER APPRECIATION PROGRAM It is free to join the "Dog Grooming Bonus Club." Beginning with your dog's first full grooming, you begin to collect stamps leading to a free grooming.
Age Requirement: Anyone

Dog Trainers

Bark Busters Home Dog Training
www.barkbusters.com
1-800-418-4584

INFORMATION This company began in Australia and there are Canadian franchises. Their website features a dog behaviour on-line quiz and training tips. It's worth a look and it won't cost you a thing!

Cat Sitting Service

The Cat Lady
451-3384 (Joan)

INFORMATION This senior-friendly cat-sitting company is a long-time advertiser in the *Edmonton Senior*. So if you're travelling and plan to leave your cat behind, let your pet enjoy the comfort of its own home. Member of the Better Business Bureau.

AFFORDABLE Competitive rates and loving care.
Age Requirement: Anyone

Pet Shows and Expos

Some consumer shows for pet owners are:
* *Edmonton Pet Expo* (January)
* *Edmonton Kennel Club Dog Shows* (April and September)
* *Edmonton Cat Fanciers Club Shows* (spring and fall)

Seniors 65-plus generally get a break on admission to these shows.

Off-Leash Areas To Walk Your Dog

Here are some off-leash areas where you can walk your dog!

OFF-LEASH AREAS – EDMONTON

The City of Edmonton publishes a great brochure entitled *Parks For Paws* that outlines over 40 off-leash sites where your dog can run and play. Area maps with boundaries are posted at each sites. Some of the areas are within neighbourhoods while others are within the river valley park system. Call 496-1475 for information on the neighbourhood sites and 496-2950 for information on the river valley sites. The City of Edmonton website also has information and it can be accessed at www.edmonton.ca.

OFF-LEASH AREAS – SHERWOOD PARK

The Regional Off-Leash Site is located three kilometres south of Wye Road on Highway 21, and left to Township Road 522. Further information from the County of Strathcona website at www.strathcona.ab.ca.

OFF-LEASH AREAS – SPRUCE GROVE

There is a 20-acre site located on Century Road plus another site in Heritage Grove Park. Further information is available from the City of Spruce Grove Parks and Recreation at 962-2611.

OFF-LEASH AREAS – STONY PLAIN

Dog owners in Stony Plain can head for the Stony Plain & District Dog Rump Creek Station in Rotary Park at 4815 – 44 Avenue. Further information: 963-4545.

The City of Leduc administrates the "K-9 Off Leash Park" for residents and their dogs. Call the City of Leduc Parks, Recreation & Culture Department for further information at 980-7116.

Book Stores – New Books

Audreys Books Ltd.
www.audreysbooks.com
10702 Jasper Avenue; 423-3487

INFORMATION Their loyalty club, "Audreys Book Club," is a point accumulation program based on purchases. You can use points for future purchases (e.g. 250 points earns a $20 store credit). You can enroll right at the store.

AFFORDABLE There is a one-time initiation fee of $5 per person to join.

Age Requirement: Anyone

Chapters, Indigo, Coles and SmithBooks
www.chapters.indigo.ca

LOYALTY REWARDS PROGRAM Their loyalty club is called "iRE-WARDS." An annual membership entitles members to a 10 per cent discount at all four bookstores on all book and audio-books (except during selected promotional periods). Members also receive a five per cent discount on all books and audio-books (except used and out-of-print books) at chapters.indigo.ca. You can join on-line or at any of the bookstores.

SAVE Senior annual membership is $20 (Adult $25).

LOCATED IN EDMONTON

- Chapters, 10504 – 82 Avenue, 435-1290
- Chapters, 3227 Calgary Trail, 431-9694
- Chapters, 9952 – 170 Street, 487-6500
- Chapters, 1384 West Edmonton Mall, 444-2555
- Coles, Londonderry Mall, 478-1414
- Coles, Bonnie Doon Shopping Centre, 466-3269
- Coles, Kingsway Garden Mall, 474-0235
- Coles, Mill Woods Town Centre, 450-9796
- Coles, Northwood Mall, 475-1797

- Coles, Southgate Shopping Centre, 436-1783
- Coles, West Edmonton Mall, 444-2082
- Indigo, 1837 – 99 Street, 432-4488
- SmithBooks, Edmonton City Centre, 425-0854

LOCATED IN SHERWOOD PARK
- Chapters, 2020 Sherwood Drive, 449-3331

LOCATED IN ST. ALBERT
- Chapters, 445 St. Albert Road, 419-7114

LOCATED IN SPRUCE GROVE
- Coles, Westland Market Mall, 962-9355
  Age Requirement: 65-plus for senior pricing on membership

Christian Book & Record
13042 – 82 Street; 478-2798
SAVE Senior customers receive a 10 per cent discount on most products, every day.
Age Requirement: 65-plus

Greenwoods' Bookshoppe
7925 – 104 Street in Edmonton; 439-2005
SAVE Seniors get a 10 per cent discount, every day (including special orders).
Age Requirement: 65-plus

Card Shops and Gift Shops

Carlton Cards
www.carltoncards.com
SAVE Seniors get a 10 per cent discount on regularly-priced merchandise every day.
CUSTOMER APPRECIATION PROGRAM "The Club Card" program is free to join. After your card is stamped for ten card purchases, you get a card free (greeting card valued up to $4).

LOCATED IN EDMONTON
- 2125 West Edmonton Mall; 486-4298
- 1628 West Edmonton Mall; 444-2074
- Londonderry Mall; 472-1083
- Bonnie Doon Shopping Centre; 469-7997

- 20 Edmonton City Centre; 423-2849
- Kingsway Garden Mall; 474-9459
- Mill Woods Town Centre; 461-6263
- Southgate Shopping Centre; 438-3520
- Westmount Shopping Centre; 488-9370

LOCATED IN ST. ALBERT
- St. Albert Centre; 458-0434

LOCATED IN SPRUCE GROVE
- Westland Market Mall; 962-8079
  Age Requirement: 65-plus for senior discount; anyone for
  "The Club Card" program

Chicken Scratch
10466 – 82 Avenue; 433-9344

LOYALTY PROGRAM You can start a "Frequent Buyer's Stamp
Card" (they are free) and once you have purchased ten
greeting cards, you receive a greeting card free up to a
$3.50 value.
Age Requirement: Anyone

Crazy 8's
www.crazy-eights.com

INFORMATION Cards, stationery, party supplies, seasonal decora-
tions and giftware.

SAVE Tuesday is "Seniors' Day" and senior customers receive 10
per cent off purchases.

LOCATED IN EDMONTON
13653 St. Albert Trail; 488-8885

LOCATED IN SHERWOOD PARK
- #15, 1020 Sherwood Drive; 464-1098
  Age Requirement: 55-plus

Crimson Quill Gifts
110, 8 Perron Street in St. Albert; 418-7803

LOYALTY REWARDS CLUB Ask for a "Preferred Customer Card."
This store keeps track of your purchases and points for you;
after you reach the required level, you receive $20 off your

next purchase (and you can start another card!). Free to join.

Age Requirement: Anyone

Hallmark
www.hallmark.com

INFORMATION Note that senior discounts are on regular-priced merchandise in most cases. The days earmarked for senior discounts, the discount percentage and the eligibility age are different at each store.

LOCATED IN EDMONTON

- Riverbend Square; 437-5756; Note that this is a combined Hallmark/Laura Secord shop and the senior discount applies to both Hallmark and Laura Secord products. (Thursdays, 15 per cent discount, 65-plus)
- Southgate Shopping Centre; 434-1549 (Every day, 10 per cent discount, 65-plus)
- South Edmonton Common; 433-1236 (Thursdays, 10 per cent discount, 65-plus)
- Kingsway Garden Mall; 474-3410 (Thursdays, 10 per cent discount, 65-plus)
- Capilano Shopping Centre; 469-2211; Note that this is a Hallmark/Embellish store. (Every day, 20 per cent discount, 55-plus)
- Mill Woods Town Centre; 461-2778 (Thursdays, 15 per cent discount, 65-plus)
- Bonnie Doon Shopping Centre; 469-8595 (Mondays/ Tuesdays/Wednesdays, 10 per cent discount, 65-plus)
- Callingwood Crossing; 443-2184 (Thursdays, 15 per cent discount, 65-plus)
- 13650 – 137 Avenue; 473-4582 (Thursdays, 15 per cent discount, 60-plus)

LOCATED IN SHERWOOD PARK

- Sherwood Park Mall; 467-4730 (Every day, 10 per cent discount, 65-plus)

- 112, 392 St. Albert Road; 419-7487 (Thursdays, 15 per cent discount, 55-plus)

Le Papier
10352 – 82 Avenue; 431-0322

LOYALTY PROGRAM This shop's "Bonus Card" (they are free) means that once you purchase 10 greeting cards, you receive a greeting card free (up to $3.50 value). When the entire stamp card is filled, you receive a discount of 15 per cent on your next purchase for both cards and other items in the shop.
Age Requirement: Anyone

Things Engraved
INFORMATION Engravable gift items such as frames and mugs and embroidery on products such as towels and blankets.

SAVE Senior customers receive a 10 per cent discount, every day.

- Edmonton City Centre; 421-0838
- Bonnie Doon Shopping Centre; 485-0235
- Londonderry Mall; 473-1758
- Southgate Shopping Centre; 434-4610
- West Edmonton Mall; 444-1061

- Sherwood Park Mall; 416-5444
  Age Requirement: 65-plus

Chapter 11

Miscellaneous Discounts and Savings

Coupon Books

Many Edmonton and area service clubs, amateur sports teams, non-profit groups and associations and schools sell copies of the *Entertainment Book* and the *Student Union Ticket Pak* as fundraising ventures.

Both coupon books are packed with savings for such regional businesses as restaurants, automotive services, ski areas and entertainment options such as movies. The *Entertainment Book* (www.entertainment.com) sells for $45 and is good from November to November each year. The *Student Union Ticket Pack* coupon book (www.sutp.com) sells for $20 and is good for September to September each year. One group that sells the *Entertainment Book* in Edmonton is the Bissell Centre. Check with your grandchildren or great-grandchildren to see if their school is selling the *Student Union Ticket Pak*. Both books are loaded with great value and can be used for savings by anyone ... including seniors! You will find offers such as "20 per cent off purchase", "One complimentary menu item when a second menu item of equal or greater value is purchased" and "Enjoy one complimentary admission when one admission is purchased." Some restrictions apply on coupon use, but any exceptions are clearly indicated and easy to understand.

Tips for using these coupon books: carry them in your vehicle so you'll always have access to them (no leaving them at home!). Familiarize yourself with the offers so you can plan ahead.

Ladies, you might carry a coupon book in a special section of your handbag.

Major Loyalty Reward Programs

Air Miles Program
www.airmiles.ca
1-888-AIR MILES

INFORMATION It is free to join the Air Miles Program. You can enroll on-line or by calling their toll-free telephone number. Reward miles can be collected from many companies on purchases of gas, groceries and merchandise and can be redeemed for travel, leisure, entertainment or merchandise rewards. Throughout this book, there is reference made to companies who are Air Mile sponsors!
Age Requirement: Anyone

Residents of Edmonton and area can collect Air Miles at the following sponsors:
- *Financial*: Bank of Montreal
- *Grocery Stores*: Safeway
- *Auto*: Goodyear, Speed Auto Glass
- *Furniture*: La-Z-Boy Furniture Galleries
- *Home Centres*: Rona, Totem Building Supplies
- *Gasoline*: Shell, Turbo
- *Miscellaneous*: Edmonton Sun, Framing & Art Centre, Iris Optometrist, Preferred Alberta Liquor Stores, Safeway Liquor Store, Sport Chek, The Shoe Company, United Van Lines

Alberta Motor Association "Show Your Card & Save" Program
INFORMATION You must be a member of the AMA and have your membership card to participate in this program. AMA will provide you with a booklet explaining the program, which provides savings of 10, 20 or 30 per cent at major businesses and services. Shown here are the categories (and names

of business and services) that would benefit AMA members residing in Edmonton and surrounding communities:

- *Cellular phones*: Bell Cellular
- *Automotive*: Groat Road Auto Service, Ming Shine/Dent Shop, Mr. Lube, Rocky's Battery, Sherlock's Automotive Repair, Speedy Glass, Vic's Service Ltd.
- *Car Rental*: Hertz
- *Bowling*: Bonnie Doon Bowling Centre, Bronx Bowl, Callingwood Lanes, Fraser Bowling Centre, Gateway Entertainment Centre, Plaza Bowl, Red's Entertainment Complex Bowling, Leduc Lanes, Sherwood Park Bowl, St. Albert Bowling Centre
- *Movie Theatres*: Cineplex Odeon/Galaxy Cinemas (Note: when using this promotion on admission savings, you must do so at an AMA office location, not at the box offices of the movie theatres.)
- *Attractions*: admissions at Devonian Botanic Garden, Father Lacombe Chapel, The Fort Saskatchewan Museum, Reynolds-Alberta Museum, Royal Alberta Museum, Rutherford House, Telus World of Science, Ukrainian Cultural Heritage Village
- *Eyewear*: LensCrafters, Pearle Vision
- *Golf*: Golden West Golf Course
- *Locksmiths*: All-Lock Rescue Ltd.
- *Van Lines/Movers*: AMJ Campbell Van Lines and
- Stallion Van Lines
- *Miscellaneous*: Cloverdale Paint, Creative Door (Garage) Services, Grower Direct, Payless Shoe Source, Sentinel Self Storage, Shoemakers Quality Shoe Repair, Voxcom, Park 'N Fly Edmonton

AMA offices in Edmonton:

- Edmonton South Centre – 10310 – 39 A Avenue; 430-5555
- Kingsway Centre -11220 – 109 Street; 474-8601
- Manning Drive Centre – 5040 Manning Drive; 473-3112
- Terra Losa Centre, 9780 – 170 Street; 484-1221

Obtaining Toll-Free Telephone Numbers – Free!

Many hotels, attractions and large companies have toll-free numbers here in Alberta and also across Canada. If you dial *1-800-555-1212*, you can ask the operator for an organisation's toll-free number (e.g. for the Banff Springs Hotel); if there is one, the operator will provide it to you at no charge. By using this toll-free number, you are saving money on long-distance telephone charges!

Dry Cleaning

Drycleaners sometimes run promotions offering money-saving coupons to customers: keep your eyes open for these types of coupons (e.g. one item cleaned at regular price and second item at half-price).

Many of the dry cleaning establishments in Edmonton and area offer free pick-up and delivery. Remember to ask if they offer these services as this saves you gas money and time.

Here are many dry cleaners that offer senior specials:

The Cleaning Centre

INFORMATION You must specifically ask for this discount when you pick up your cleaning order.

SAVE All locations of The Cleaning Centre offer 15 per cent off, every day.

Age Requirement: 65-plus

LOCATED IN EDMONTON
- 101, 17628 – 103 Avenue; 489-7293
- 14740 – 40 Avenue; 430-6921

LOCATED IN SHERWOOD PARK
- 29 Broadmoor Baseline Crossing; 417-1211

LOCATED IN ST. ALBERT
- 34, 11 Bellerose Drive; 460-9110

LOCATED IN SPRUCE GROVE
- 40, 100 Campsite Road; 960-6807

Fabric Care Cleaners & Launderers

SAVE All locations offer a 10 per cent discount, every day.

Age Requirement: 65-plus

- 17520 – 108 Avenue; 483-7500
- Callingwood Shopping Centre; 487-2731
- Bonnie Doon Shopping Centre; 466-9927
- Southgate Shopping Centre; 434-2613
- Riverbend Road/45 Avenue; 435-5526

- 205, 10 McKenny Avenue; 419-3255

Grove Drycleaners
200 McLeod Avenue in Spruce Grove; 962-0777
SAVE Senior discount of 10 per cent, always.
Age Requirement: 65-plus

Page The Cleaner
Not all locations offer senior discounts but the following do.
SAVE Senior customers save 10 per cent, every day, on their cleaning orders.
Age Requirement: 65-plus

- 5124 – 122 Street; 435-3211
- 8525 – 109 Street; 433-7666
- 6127 – 28 Avenue; 450-6599
- Capilano Shopping Centre; 465-6622
- Millbourne Market Mall; 451-1006
- 2331 – 66 Street; 461-4760
- Edmonton City Centre; 421-7694
- 11765 Jasper Avenue; 488-4312

- Sherwood Park Mall; 467-0191
- 14, 140 Athabascan Avenue

The Press Gallery
www.pressgallery.ab.ca

INFORMATION The downtown location at 94 Street and Jasper
Avenue offers a convenient drive-through drop-off window!
SAVE Seniors save 10 per cent off their cleaning orders, every day
Age Requirement: 65-plus

LOCATED IN EDMONTON
- 9440 Jasper Avenue; 49-PRESS (497-7377)
- Kingsway Garden Mall; 474-6240
- 11729 Jasper Avenue at *Devine Custom Tailors*; 497-7377
- 12959 – 97 Street at *Formals By Page*; 497-7377

Price Drycleaners
115 First Avenue in Spruce Grove; 962-9622
SAVE Senior discount of 10 per cent, always.
Age Requirement: 65-plus

Swan Dry Cleaners
Leduc Towne Square in Leduc; 986-8882
SAVE Senior discount of 10 per cent, every day.
Age Requirement: 65-plus

Clothing Gifts For Grandchildren and Great-Grandchildren

The two shops of Kids "R" Special Clothing offer a 10 per
cent discount on purchases to senior customers every Monday.
They retail a nice variety of clothing for children from newborn
to age 12.
- Westmount Shopping Centre; 455-1170
- Capilano Shopping Centre; 490-4760
Age Requirement: 65-plus

Community Leagues in Edmonton

A search of the Edmonton Federation of Community Leagues
website (www.efcl.org) shows that some community leagues offer
substantial annual membership discounts to seniors living in the
community. Here are some examples:
- *Baturyn Community League*: senior membership $10 (family
membership $25)

- *Beacon Heights Community League*: senior membership $10 (family membership $25)
- *La Pearle Community League*: senior membership $20 (family membership $30)
- *Ritchie Community League*: senior membership free (family membership $20)

So, check directly with the community league for the community you reside in (there are 147 community leagues in Edmonton but not all offer senior annual membership discounts); if your community league offers senior discounts, ask about the qualifying age.

Congratulatory Scrolls

FREE Staff at the Legislative Assembly of Alberta will coordinate the offering of congratulatory scrolls to mark 65th and upwards milestone birthdays and 25th, 50th and 60th anniversaries. At least one month's notice is required.

INFORMATION You can call 427-2826 or order online by visiting their website at www.assembly.ab.ca, then clicking on "Public Information" and accessing "Congratulatory Scrolls."

Florists

Safeway Florist

INFORMATION Safeway grocery stores have floral departments and on the first Tuesday of every month, you can save on plants, fresh-cut flowers and arrangements in their floral cooler (discount does not apply to FTD orders or phone orders).

INFORMATION Safeway is an Air Miles sponsor.

SAVE 10 per cent on floral purchases or 10 times the Air Miles on the first Tuesday of each month.

There are 19 stores in Edmonton, two stores in Sherwood Park, two stores in St. Albert and one store in each of the communities of Spruce Grove, Stony Plain and Leduc.

Grower Direct

INFORMATION Their yellow page advertisement shows that they participate in the "Show Your Card and Save Program" which provides you with savings on floral purchases if you are a member of the Alberta Motor Association. There are nine locations in Edmonton; two in Sherwood Park and one in St. Albert. You can collect Aeroplan Miles at Grower Direct.

Photo Finishing

Black's Photography
www.blackphoto.com

LOYALTY PROGRAM A brand-new loyalty program is being introduced in January of 2006. Memberships in the current "Black's Reward Club" still continue to enjoy the same savings and benefits until their expiry in the program; however, no new memberships are being offered in this particular loyalty program.

SAVE Senior customers who make in-store orders for photofinishing receive a 10 per cent discount, always.

LOCATED IN EDMONTON

- Bonnie Doon Shopping Centre; 469-7219
- Kingsway Garden Mall; 477-7086
- Southgate Shopping Centre; 437-4172
- West Edmonton Mall; 444-1296
- Mill Woods Town Centre; 461-4073
  Age Requirement: 60-plus

Japan Camera
www.japancamera.com
   1011 West Edmonton Mall; 444-1370

LOYALTY PROGRAM You can join the "JPoints" program free and earn points with purchases. You receive "free points" when you join and a free JPrint Digital Print. As a member, you will automatically receive notice of promotional offers as they become available and you can redeem points for products and services.

Age Requirement: Anyone

Major Department Stores

The Bay
www.hbc.com

SAVE The first Tuesday of every month is "Seniors' Day" and senior customers receive 10 per cent off purchases.

LOYALTY PROGRAM The HBC Rewards Program is free to join (you can join at Customer Service at any store or online). Points are earned on purchases and customers can redeem points for merchandise such as housewares and electronics from the *HBC Rewards Catalogue.*
Age Requirement: 60-plus for "Seniors' Day"; Anyone for the loyalty program.

LOCATED IN EDMONTON
- Edmonton City Centre; 424-0151
- Kingsway Garden Mall; 479-7100
- Londonderry Mall; 478-2931
- Southgate Shopping Centre; 435-9211
- West Edmonton Mall; 444-1550

LOCATED IN ST. ALBERT
- St. Albert Centre; 458-5800

Home Oufitters
www.hbc.com

INFORMATION This department store-size chain specializes in home fashions and kitchen/bath merchandise.

LOYALTY PROGRAM The HBC Rewards Program is free to join (you can join at the store or online). Points are earned on purchases and customers can redeem points for merchandise such as housewares and electronics from the *HBC Rewards Catalogue.*

There are four Home Outfitter stores located in Edmonton.
- 9738 – 19 Avenue; 414-5850
- 13554 – 137 Avenue; 456-8006
- 17531 Stony Plain Road; 496-9354
- 220 Edmonton City Centre; 701-0162

Zellers

www.hbc.com

SAVE The first Monday of every month is "Seniors' Day" and senior customers receive a 10 per cent discount off their purchases (some exceptions apply). As well, several promotions in which seniors 55-plus can save 10 per cent are run every few months over-and-above the usual first Monday of every month (for example, on a Tuesday); watch for advertising in newspapers.

LOYALTY PROGRAM The HBC Rewards Program is free to join (you can join at Customer Service at any of the stores or online). Points are earned for purchases and customers can redeem points for merchandise such as housewares and electronics from the *HBC Rewards Catalogue.*

LOCATED IN EDMONTON
- Westmount Shopping Centre; 455-3131
- Abbottsfield Shoppers Mall; 474-8027
- Bonnie Doon Shopping Centre; 461-6776
- 3931 Calgary Trail; 436-2211
- Kingsway Garden Mall; 479-8414
- Meadowlark Shopping Centre; 484-1171
- West Edmonton Mall; 444-1722
- Millwoods Town Centre; 468-7050
- Northwood Mall; 473-3828

LOCATED IN SHERWOOD PARK
- Sherwood Park Mall; 467-7755

LOCATED IN ST. ALBERT
- St. Albert Centre; 459-6641
  Age Requirement: 55-plus for "Seniors Day"; Anyone for loyalty program.

Medium-Sized Department Stores

Army & Navy Department Stores

SAVE The first Tuesday of every month is "Seniors' Day" and senior customers receive a 15 per discount on purchases.
Age Requirement: 60-plus

LOCATED IN EDMONTON
- 10411 – 82 Avenue; 433-5503
- Londonderry Shopping Centre; 456-1155

Fields
SAVE "Seniors' Day" is the first Monday of every month and seniors receive a 10 per cent discount on purchases.

LOCATED IN EDMONTON
- Millbourne Shopping Centre; 485-2709

LOCATED IN LEDUC
- 5302 – 50 Street; 986-5654
  Age Requirement: 55-plus

SAAN Stores
www.saan.ca
SAVE "Seniors' Day" is the first Monday of every month and senior customers save 10 per cent on purchases.

LOCATED IN EDMONTON
- 12520 – 137 Avenue; 455-5309
- 400, 6655 – 178 Street; 487-2763

LOCATED IN STONY PLAIN
- 5007 – 48 Street; 963-9240

LOCATED IN LEDUC
- Leduc Town Square; 986-6403

Womens' Clothing Stores

Penningtons
www.penningtons.com
SAVE "Seniors' Day" is held the first Tuesday of every month and customers receive 15 per cent off purchases.
LOYALTY REWARDS CLUB The "PS Club Advantage Program" is free to join. Each time you accumulate $500 in purchases, they will mail you a $25 gift certificate (the store keeps track of all this for you). Members of the program also receive regular notice of upcoming sales events in their stores. You can apply to be a member at any of their stores.

Age Requirement: 60-plus for "Seniors' Day" discounts;
Anyone for the "PS Club Advantage Program."

LOCATED IN EDMONTON
- 13816 – 40 Street; 475-8094
- 200 Mayfield Common; 489-2851
- 3903 Calgary Trail; 437-9685
- 12222 – 137 Avenue; 475-5782

LOCATED IN SHERWOOD PARK
- 993 Fir Street; 416-3624

Discount Stores and Second Hand Stores Offering Senior Discounts

Bargain, Bargain
11810 – 103 Street; 479-2367

INFORMATION This store retails new housewares, clothing, cards
and wrap and some beauty products at bargain prices.

SAVE Every Monday is "Seniors' Day" and seniors receive 10 per
cent off regularly-priced merchandise.
Age Requirement: 60-plus

You can find good value and low pricing on gently-used
clothing, books, sportswear, housewares and small appliances
at second hand stores in Edmonton and area. Several of these
second-hand stores do offer senior discounts (savings on top of
savings!) and they are listed here:

Goodwill G-Mart Stores
SAVE Senior customers receive 10 per cent off purchases every
day.

LOCATED IN EDMONTON
- 8759 – 51 Avenue; 944-0243
- 15020 Stony Plain Road; 944-0563
- 10455 – 80 Avenue; 944-1041
- 11720 – 34 Street; 944-0059
Age Requirement: 60-plus with ID

Salvation Army Thrift Stores
SAVE Senior customers receive 20 per cent off purchases on Tuesdays, always.

LOCATED IN EDMONTON
- 5804 Terrace Road; 469-8291
- 10131 Princess Elizabeth Avenue; 477-1599
- 9503 – 49 Street; 432-6751
- 12928 – 50 Street; 475-8778
- 10901 – 82 Avenue; 439-6750

LOCATED IN SHERWOOD PARK
- 10 Main Boulevard; 416-1303

LOCATED IN ST. ALBERT
- 2003 Tudor Glen; 458-7638

LOCATED IN LEDUC
- 4911 – 50 Avenue; 986-8861
  Age Requirement: 60-plus with ID

Value Village
SAVE Tuesday is "Seniors' Day" and senior customers receive 30 per cent off their purchases.

LOCATED IN EDMONTON
- 8930 – 82 Avenue; 468-1259
- 9540 – 163 Street; 484-4177
- 11850 – 103 Street; 477-0025
- 10127 – 34 Avenue; 414-5859
  Age Requirement: 62-plus

Knife Sharpening

House of Knives
www.houseofknives.ca
Kingsway Garden Mall in Edmonton; 477-6504
SAVE Senior customers receive 10 per cent off knife sharpening and regular-priced items, every day.
Age Requirement: 65-plus with ID.

Moving Companies

If a move to another home, condominium or apartment in the Edmonton area is in your future, or if you are re-locating out of Edmonton for your retirement years, you will need the services of a moving company.

The following companies indicate in their yellow page advertisements that they offer senior discounts (some also offer mid-month discounts and some companies offer both). Others do not offer senior discounts, but are Air Mile sponsors. You will need to ask what the age requirement is to qualify for the senior discount.

Because the variables of a move are so complex (e.g. local move versus long distance move; or whether you pack or they do) the best way is to talk and work directly with these moving companies.

- *AAA Best Way Movers*; 469-7600 ("mid-month discount"; local and long distance moves).
- *A Al's Piano & Furniture Moving*; 468-5244 ("senior discount"; local and Calgary moves).
- *A Certified Moving Ltd.*; 465-7000 ("senior discount" and a "mid-month discount"; local and long distance moves).
- *A Class Movers*; 485-9998 ("senior discount" and a "mid-month discount"; local and long distance moves).
- *Action Moving*; 474-2861 ("mid-month discount"; local and long distance moves).
- *A Quality Movers Ltd.*; 461-6800 ("senior discount" and a "mid-month discount"; local and long distance service within Western Canada).
- *AMJ Campbell Van Lines/Atlas Van Lines*; 453-6946 ("senior discount" and participation in the Alberta Motor Association "Show Your Card and Save" Program for AMA members; local and long distance moves).
- *A Safeway Moving Ltd.*; 437-9999 ("mid-month discount"; local and long distance moves).
- *Big Town Moving*; 461-9978 ("senior discount" and a "mid-month discount); local and long distance moves).

- *Davis Moving & Storage*; 482-1991 in Edmonton and 459-3996 in St. Albert ("senior discount"; local and long distance moving).
- *Dolly's Furniture Relocators*; 463-2281 ("senior discount" and a "mid-month discount"; local and long distance moves).
- *Dorcy's Moving Ltd.*; 436-1274 ("senior local moving discounts"; local and long distance moves).
- *Eager Beaver Moving*; 434-1100 ("senior discount"; local and long distance moves).
- *Highland Moving and Storage Ltd./United Van Lines*; 453-6777 (Air Mile sponsor; local and long distance moving)
- *King George Van Lines*; 444-6373 ("senior discount"; long distance service in Alberta and B.C.)
- *Matco Moving/North American Van Lines*; 484-8800 (Air Mile Sponsor; local and long distance moves).
- *No Fuss Moving & Storage*; 455-6333 ("senior discount"; local and long distance moves).
- *Precision Piano Moving & Storage Ltd.*; 468-9145 ("senior discount"; local moves).
- *Provincial Moving & Storage Ltd.*; 469-6233 ("senior discount"; local and long distance moves).
- *Two Amigos & Company*; 450-6797 ("senior discount"; local and long distance moves).
- *Western Moving & Storage/Allied Van Lines*; 423-6835 ("senior discount"; local and long distance moves).

Storage Unit Facilities

If you need to rent storage space, there are many facilities to choose from in the Edmonton area. You will probably choose a storage facility close to home for easy access. Some facilities offer 24-hour-per-day access, seven days a week. Some offer computerized access, resident site managers, both unheated and heated units or video surveillance.

Sentinel Self-Storage participates in the Alberta Motor Association's "Show Your Card and Save Program"; they have six locations in Edmonton.

The yellow page advertisements for the following five companies indicate that they offer a "senior discount." You will need to check with them directly about the eligibility age for these discounts and about the discount itself:

STORAGE UNIT FACILITIES – EDMONTON

- *Guardian Storage* (14350 – 111 Avenue; 732-5000)
- *Pay-Less Self-Storage* (14630 – 128 Avenue; 732-5377)
- *Storage Centre* (7903 Argyll Road; 463-2281)
- *Wildrose Self Storage* (19121 – 118 A Avenue; 451-3302)

STORAGE UNIT FACILITIES – SHERWOOD PARK

- *All Store Storage* (beside Millennium Place; 416-1114)

Many companies have yellow page advertisements (listed under "Storage Household") indicating that there are savings available on:

- Discounts on six-month to one-year contracts;
- Long-term discounts;
- Pre-paid discounts; and/or
- Mid-month discounts.

Bottled Water/Water Cooler Units

The yellow page advertisement for the *Arrowhead Premium Drinking Water* company indicates that they offer "senior discounts." Their website is www.arrowheadwater.ca and they can be reached at 486-2467. You will need to enquire about the eligibility age for the discount.

Information on Funeral Planning

Alberta Funeral Services Regulatory Board
452-6130

INFORMATION This board is responsible for providing funeral information to the general public, licensing and monitoring funeral homes and crematoriums and responding to questions/service concerns from consumers.

FREE You can request a copy of their free booklet entitled *Funeral Planning In Alberta*.

Chapter 12

Health & Beauty

This chapter outlines some savings in the area of health. You can save at places including drug stores, health food/vitamin stores and stores that sell eyewear. It will also touch on grocery store health tours. Need a haircut or trim? You'll discover lots of hair salons and barber shops that offer senior prices on their services.

When people discuss health costs, the topic of prescription drugs is often at the forefront. Prescription drugs, however, are never discounted. The only option for saving in this area is if the prescription drug your doctor has prescribed is available in a generic version. Discuss this with your regular pharmacist. The pharmacies of most drug stores *offer free delivery* on prescription orders.

Most of today's drug stores have a good array of health-related brochures and publications that are free for you to take home and read.

Some drug stores are "pharmacy centres" meaning that they have a pharmacy and some OTC (over-the-counter) medications such as aspirin and cold remedies but very few "store-front" items such as magazines, shampoo and beauty products. Many of the larger drug stores have a pharmacy and over-the-counter medications plus a huge inventory of store-front items (some of these larger drug stores even have photo departments).

Sometimes you will hear some people say that their chiropractor, hearing aid provider or denturist gave them a seniors' discount or a free service such as a "free denture cleaning". These health care and health service suppliers (and others such as massage therapists) operate independently, so you will need to check personally with your own service supplier to see whether or not they offer a senior discount or free service.

A good general reference book on health has recently been published by Alberta Business Research Ltd. It is entitled *A Guide To Healthy Living For People 50+ in Alberta*. The 230-page book ($18.69) helps seniors target health to get more out of life, become healthier, live longer and be happier through healthy living. There is excellent information on learning more through associations and specific health authorities. To order or for more information, call (780) 425-7463.

Drug Stores with Seniors' Days and/or Discounts

Drugstore "Seniors' Day" or "senior discounts" do not apply to prescriptions. Also excluded are purchases of lottery tickets, stamps and tobacco, and sometimes, there are other exceptions. The discount (in most cases) is applied to regular price merchandise (not sale merchandise). But the good news is that besides covering medicines like non-prescription cold medication or antacids, the discounts also apply to items like bandages and tissues, greeting cards and even chocolate bars and gum!

Many of the larger drugstore chains (such as Guardian, Rexall, IDA, plus ARP) have prescription centre locations. These are smaller stores that are "pharmacy-focused" and therefore do not carry a large selection of store-front merchandise. Prescription centre locations are not included here.

There are pharmacy/over-the-counter drug departments in Safeway, Save-On-Foods and some of the Sobeys branches. On over-the-counter items, you can save on the grocery chain's monthly saving day (see Chapter 1 *Food and Beverage*).

Corner ARP Pharmacy
15557 Stony Plain Road in Edmonton; 489-5526

SAVE Each Wednesday is "Senior Day" with 10 per cent off store-front products (some exceptions apply).
Age Requirement: 55-plus

Delton ARP Pharmacy
12930 – 82 Street in Edmonton; 476-8737
SAVE Each Tuesday is "Senior Day" with 10 per cent off store-front products (some exceptions apply).
Age Requirement: 65-plus

Guardian Drugs
14061 Victoria Trail in Edmonton; 473-0832
SAVE Senior customers receive a 10 per cent discount on store-front products, every day (some exceptions apply).
Age Requirement: 55-plus

Guardian Drugs
111, 200 Boudreau Road in St. Albert; 459-1128
SAVE Senior customers receive a 10 per cent discount on store-front products, every day (some exceptions apply).
Age Requirement: 65-plus

London Drugs
www.ldhealth.com

LOCATED IN EDMONTON
- North Town Mall; 944-4521
- 14951 Stony Plain Road; 944-4522
- 10531 – 51 Avenue; 944-4523
- 11704 – 104 Avenue; 944-4545
- West Edmonton Mall; 944-4526
- South Edmonton Common; 944-4557

LOCATED IN SHERWOOD PARK
- 999 Fir Street; 944-4520

LOCATED IN ST. ALBERT
- 19 Bellerose Drive; 944-4548

SAVE Coupons in the *We Scan You Save* coupon books (available in-store or online) provide savings on specific products throughout the store and new coupon books are produced on a regular basis throughout the year.

INFORMATION Their website has a link to *London Drugs Health* which includes a health library, a condition centre plus information on the categories of health tools and personal health.

FREE Pharmacies at London Drugs stores offer free copies of *Focus On Better Care* magazine (published several times per year). You can also receive the magazine at home free by subscription – simply fill out and mail the form found inside the magazine.
Age Requirement: Anyone

Millwoods Value Drug Mart
6428 – 28 Avenue in Edmonton; 463-8833
SAVE Seniors receive a 10 per cent discount, every day, on regular priced store-front merchandise (some exceptions apply).
Age Requirement: 65-plus

Primrose IDA Pharmacy
8462 – 182 Street in Edmonton; 487-7270
SAVE Seniors receive a 10 per cent discount on store-front products, every day (some exceptions apply).
Age Requirement: 65-plus

Rexall Drug Stores
The Rexall Drug Stores listed here offer a 10 per cent discount to seniors every day on regular priced store-front items (prescriptions, tobacco and some other items are excluded). The age requirement varies, but is noted below for each individual location.

FREE You can pick up a copy of the *Health and Lifestyle* quarterly magazine at participating Rexall Drug Stores (while quantities last). Each issue focuses on health and wellness, fitness and nutrition, and features a column written by a pharmacist.

LOCATED IN EDMONTON
- Capilano Mall; 466-1744 (age requirement: 65-plus)

- 10228 – 142 Street; 454-6403 (age requirement: 65-plus)
- 9228 – 144 Avenue; 478-4641 (age requirement: 55-plus)
- 11036 – 51 Avenue; 434-7120 (age requirement: 65-plus)
- Southgate Shopping Centre; 434-0451 (age requirement: 55-plus)
- 11229 Jasper Avenue; 488-4665 (age requirement: 65-plus)
- 11811 Jasper Avenue; 482-2360 (age requirement: 55-plus)

LOCATED IN LEDUC
- 4906 – 50 Avenue; 986-8313 (age requirement: 65-plus)

Shopper's Drug Mart
www.shoppersdrugmart.ca

SAVE A "Senior Day" is held once a month and is well advertised. Seniors receive a discount on purchases made that day (some exceptions such as prescriptions/tobacco). The age requirement varies from store to store, so check at your local store. Note that discounts on "Senior Day" may not exceed $50.

LOYALTY PROGRAM "The Optimum Club" is free to join and you can enroll at any Shopper's Drug Mart or online. You collect points for each purchase (including prescriptions but excluding tobacco, lottery and post office). An example of rewards is that when you reach the 20,000 point level, you earn a discount reward of 70 per cent off. The program has a new component called "Pay With Points": you can look for store products with the Pay With Points icon and purchase them with the required number of points instantly at the cash register.

INFORMATION The company's website has some interesting links including HealthWATCH (an ongoing program of health knowledge and advice); the Natural Health Centre (information about natural health products), Health Conditions (a source for easy-to-understand information on hundreds of medical conditions) and a "Senior Link" with articles on healthy living and monthly health news. The Shopper's Drug Mart stores located at 11408 Jasper Avenue and 8210 – 109 Street in are both open 24-hours, seven days a week.

- 17220 – 95 Avenue; 443-5800
- 13030 – 137 Avenue; 456-4330
- 13514 – 97 Street; 406-7397
- 66 Streeet and 137 Avenue; 478-2921
- 13310 – 111 Avenue; 453-5885
- 9452 – 118 Avenue; 477-1540
- Kingsway Garden Mall; 474-8237
- 16504 – 95 Street; 456-5557
- 3812 – 118 Avenue; 474-2424
- Edmonton City Centre; 426-7642
- 10200 – 102 Avenue; 428-7110
- Meadowlark Shopping Centre; 484-7718
- 6655 – 178 Street; 487-1013
- 7469 – 101 Avenue; 485-1601
- 8210 – 109 Street; 433-2424
- Bonnie Doon Shopping Centre; 469-2888
- 4619 – 91 Avenue; 468-4002
- 584 Riverbend Square; 988-6657
- Millbourne Shopping Centre; 462-4704
- 10955 – 23 Avenue; 436-3055
- 3945 – 34 Street; 461-6768
- Mill Woods Town Centre; 461-1121
- 8065 – 104 Street; 433-3954

- Sherwood Park Mall; 464-9788
- Baseline Road/Clover Bar Road; 416-1706

- 108,392 St. Albert Road; 458-5880
- 1,140 St. Albert Road; 460-9222

- 6108 – 50 Street; 986-2422

- 70 McLeod Avenue; 962-5202
- 16 Grove Plaza; 962-3555

- 400, 4300 South Park Drive; 963-6946

Vision: Eyewear

Lenscrafters
SAVE Senior customers receive a 20 per cent discount on lenses and frames every day.

INFORMATION The six Lenscrafters locations in Edmonton are open seven days a week.
- Kingsway Garden Mall; 477-3340
- Mill Woods Town Centre; 450-3285
- Southgate Shopping Centre; 437-8886
- West Edmonton Mall (Phase I); 444-3370
- West Edmonton Mall (Phase 3); 444-1110
- Westmount Shopping Centre; 455-0980
  Age requirement: 65-plus

Optical Gallery Family Eyewear
10603 – 107 Avenue in Edmonton; 424-3038

SAVE Senior customers receive discounts on lenses and frames.

INFORMATION A good selection of larger frames to suit bi-focal lenses.
Age Requirement: "Senior" (see page 3)

Health, Vitamin and Herbal Stores

Callingwood Vitamin Centre
248, 6655 – 178 Street in Edmonton; 481-0157

SAVE "Senior Day" is the first Monday of every month (if Monday is a holiday, the following Tuesday becomes the "Senior Day") and senior customers receive 15 per cent off. All other days, seniors receive 10 per cent off. Periodically, this store holds "Super Senior Days" and they will take your telephone number and call you about these promotions. Note that some exceptions apply.

INFORMATION In November, this store has an annual "Customer Appreciation Day" on which a 25 per cent discount is offered for all customers, regardless of age. Note that some exceptions apply.

Age Requirement: 65-plus for "Senior Day" and "Super
Senior Day"

Grace's Herbs 'N Things

Leduc Town Square in Leduc; 986-1075

SAVE Seniors receive a 10 per cent discount, every day, on regular
priced merchandise.

Age Requirement: 70-plus

Health 4U

- Westland Market Mall in Spruce Grove; 962-2912
- 260 King Street in Spruce Grove; 962-1313
- Meridian Village Mall in Stony Plain; 963-5556

SAVE Senior customers receive discounts every day at various
levels (e.g. supplements at 10 per cent and health/beauty
at five per cent); some exceptions apply. "Customer
Appreciation Day" is held the last Saturday of each month
and customers of any age receive 15 per cent off on most
items. Senior customers get to add on their "every day" 10
per cent or five per cent senior discount (depending on the
product) on top of that!

Age Requirement: 65-plus for senior discounts

Health Matters

9977 – 178 Street in Edmonton; 443-3335

SAVE Senior customers receive a 10 per cent discount on everything in the store, every day. The last Wednesday of each
month is "Customer Appreciation Day" on which all customers (regardless of age) receive a 25 per cent discount on
everything in the store, even on sale items.

Age Requirement: 55-plus for senior discount

Morning Sun Health Foods

SAVE On "Customer Appreciation Day," the first Tuesday of every
month, customers receive 15 per cent off purchases (except
sale items).

INFORMATION Morning Sun Health Foods has a bottle recycling
program. Bring your empty vitamin bottles into either of
their stores when coming to purchase the same product

and you will receive a rebate: 50 cents off when the vitamin product you buy retails under $10 and $1 off when the vitamin product you buy retails over $10.
Age Requirement: Anyone

LOCATED IN EDMONTON
• Mill Woods Town Centre; 468-2868

LOCATED IN SHERWOOD PARK
• Sherwood Park Mall; 449-3528

Newfound Health Stores
www.newfoundhealth.com

SAVE The following stores offer savings specific to their location; there are some exceptions that apply, so check.

INFORMATION On the website there are coupons on the website to print out for savings (see "Shop Newfound" link). There is also a link to an on-line version of their current flyer; the flyers feature "limited time bonus coupons."

LOCATED IN EDMONTON
• Edmonton City Centre at #1173 Eaton Centre; 425-9496 ("Senior Customer Appreciation Day" is the first Wednesday of every month; 25 per cent off most regular priced products and 10 per cent off sale products; 60-plus)
• Southgate Shopping Centre; 437-7997 ("Senior Customer Appreciation Day" is the first Wednesday of every month; 25 per cent off most regular priced products and 10 per cent off sale products; "senior"(see page XX for definition)
• Meadowlark Shopping Centre; 443-0878 (senior customers receive a 10 per cent discount every day on most regular priced products; 65-plus)
• Abbottsfield Mall; 474-3298 ("Senior Customer Appreciation Day" is the first Wednesday of every month; 25 per cent off most regular priced products; 65-plus)
• Mill Woods Town Centre; 468-5469 (senior customers receive a 10 per cent discount every day on most regular priced products and 10 per cent off sale products; 65-plus)
• North Town Mall at the northeast corner of 97 Street and 137 Avenue; 475-1183 (senior customers receive a 10 per

cent discount every day on most regular priced products; 65-plus)

- 1149 West Edmonton Mall; 444-1008 ("Senior Customer Appreciation Day" is the first Wednesday of every month; 25 per cent off most regular priced products and 10 per cent off sale products; 55-plus)
- 1758 West Edmonton Mall; 444-1003 ("Senior Customer Appreciation Day" is the first Wednesday of every month; 25 per cent off most regular priced products and 10 per cent off sale products; 55-plus)
- 3816 – 137 Avenue; 497-7976 (Senior customers receive a 10 per cent discount every day on most regular priced products with higher discounts offered on "Senior Customer Appreciation Day," the first Wednesday of each month; 25 per cent off most regular priced products and also a 15 per cent level discount on specific products; 65-plus)

LOCATED IN ST. ALBERT

- #220, 700 St. Albert Road; 459-7917 ("Senior Customer Appreciation Day" is the first Wednesday of every month; 25 per cent off most regular priced products and 10 per cent off on sale products; "senior" age – see page 3 for definition)

LOCATED IN SPRUCE GROVE

- #46, 96 Campsite Road; 962-9710 ("Senior Customer Appreciation Day" is the first Wednesday of every month; 10 per cent and 15 per cent discounts on specific products; 65-plus)

Optimum Health Vitamins & More

LOYALTY PROGRAM Ask for a free stamp card, good at any of their four locations. For each minimum $20 purchase you will receive a stamp plus a 10 per cent discount on regular priced merchandise (excluded are items such as books, cosmetics, clearance and sale products, etc.). When you fill the stamp card, your next purchase will be discounted at 15 per cent off (clearance items are included).

Age Requirement: Anyone

LOCATED IN EDMONTON
- 11646 – 104 Avenue; 452-5705
- 5860 – 111 Street; 439-5748
- 109 Street and 71 Avenue; 432-5464

LOCATED IN SHERWOOD PARK
- #234, 222 Baseline Village; 467-6650

Vitality Health Foods
www.vitalityhealthfoods.com

SAVE Advertising flyers feature savings coupons: "buy one product at the regular price, get the second of equal or lesser price at 50 per cent off" and "customer appreciation" discount coupons. Stores also hold periodic "no GST on regular-items" promotion days (a savings of seven per cent).
Age Requirement: Anyone

FREE Regular demonstrations/information sessions are held by leading brand representatives in all stores.

LOCATED IN EDMONTON
- Londonderry Mall; 473-4268
- Northwood Mall; 476-6062
- Westmount Shopping Centre; 453-1313
- Capilano Shopping Centre; 413-4817
- Bonnie Doon Mall; 469-3411
- Stony Plain Road/149 Street; 484-2380
- South Edmonton Common; 461-0889

LOCATED IN SHERWOOD PARK
- Sherwood Park Mall; 467-0389

LOCATED IN ST. ALBERT
- Gateway Village Centre; 460-4583

The Vitamin Farm
Edmonton City Centre, downtown; 424-2893

SAVE A senior discount of 10 per cent off purchases is offered every day.
Age Requirement: 60-plus

Hair Salons

Here are some Edmonton and area hair salons that offer senior pricing.

The Bay Premiere Beauty Salons

SAVE The six Bay Premiere Beauty Salons offer senior savings to those 65-plus (discount does not apply to beauty/hair products):

IN EDMONTON BAY STORES

- Kingsway Garden Mall; 479-7100 (Senior discount Tuesdays; 15 per cent off on hair services)
- Londonderry Mall; 478-2931 (Senior discount Mondays; 10 per cent off on hair services)
- Southgate Shopping Centre; 435-9211 (Senior discount Tuesdays; 15 per cent off on hair services)
- Edmonton City Centre; 424-0151 (Senior discount Mondays; 10 per cent off on hair services)
- West Edmonton Mall; 444-1550 (Senior discount Tuesdays; 15 per cent off on hair services)

IN ST. ALBERT BAY STORE

- St. Albert Centre; 458-5800 (Senior discount Tuesdays; 15 per cent off on hair services)

Elegance Hair Design

13 Westland Market Mall in Spruce Grove; 962-9364

SAVE Senior pricing on haircuts, every day.
Age Requirement: 65-plus

First Choice Haircutters

SAVE All eight *First Choice Haircutters* salons listed here offer a "senior basic haircut" for $9.95, every day, for customers 65-plus. In addition each salon offers its own additional senior discount as shown; seniors must be 65-plus for all offered discounts.

- 17751 – 98 A. Avenue; 489-3376 ("Senior Day" is on both Tuesday and Wednesday – 15 per cent off colours, perms and sets).
- 6124 – 28 Avenue; 450-8516 ("Senior Day" on Wednesday – 15 per cent off colours and highlights).
- 232 Manning Drive; 475-8428 ("Senior Day" is every day with senior pricing on shampoos/cuts and complete styles for short hair).
- 10379 – 112 Street; 420-0235 ("Senior Day" on Tuesday – 10 per cent discount on perms).
- 2059 – 98 Street; 433-5333 ("Senior Day" is every day with senior pricing on perms and cuts/styles).

- 367 St. Albert Road; 459-0787 ("Senior Day" is both Tuesday and Wednesday – 15 per cent discount on colours, perms and sets).
- 215, 700 St. Albert Road; 418-0117 ("Senior Day" is both Tuesday and Wednesday – 15 per cent off perms and colours).

- 24, 96C Campsite Road; 962-1716 ("Senior Day" is both Tuesday and Wednesday – 15 per cent off colours, perms and sets).

Leduc Cuts Family Hair Care
3, 4922 – 51 Avenue in Leduc; 986-6717
SAVE Senior pricing on haircuts, every day.
Age Requirement: 65-plus

Magicuts
The following five Magicut Salons offer senior pricing:

- 60 Kingsway Garden Mall in Zellers; 474-4156 (The first Monday of every month is Senior Day with senior pricing offered; 65-plus).

- Westmount Shopping Centre in Zellers; 448-3669 (The first Monday of every month is Senior Day with senior pricing offered; 65-plus).
- Northwood Shopping Centre in Zellers; 448-2390 (The first Monday of every month is Senior Day with senior pricing offered; 65-plus).

LOCATED IN SHERWOOD PARK

- Sherwood Park Mall in Zellers; 417-7557 (the first Monday of every month is Senior Day with senior pricing offered; 65-plus).

LOCATED IN LEDUC

- Leduc Town Square; 986-9559 (Customers 65-plus receive 10 per cent off all products and services each Tuesday and Wednesday; senior haircuts are 15 per cent off on the first Monday of each month).

Marquis Hair Styling
- Capilano Shopping Centre in Edmonton; 440-1200
- Londonderry Mall in Edmonton; 478-1322
- 3210 – 118 Avenue in Edmonton; 474-3333

SAVE Senior pricing on hair services, every day.
Age Requirement: 65-plus

Meridian Stylists Ltd.
123, 4401 – 48 Street in Stony Plain; 963-6154
SAVE Senior pricing on hair services, every day.
Age Requirement: 65-plus

Salon de l'Art Hair
8, 44 St. Thomas Street in St. Albert; 460-4399
SAVE Seniors save 10 per cent, always.
Age Requirement: 65-plus

Singleton's Hair Care
The following 12 Singleton's Hair Care salons offer senior pricing. Apart from the salon at Victoria Trail (see below), all the salons offer seniors 20 per cent off regular priced hair services every day, but the qualifying age varies, as shown.

- 15277 Castle Downs Road; 457-5349 (60-plus)
- 2033 – 111 Street; 435-8669 (60-plus)
- 10110 – 149 Street; 489-8491 (60-plus)
- 4210 – 66 Street; 461-6150 (60-plus. Also, on the first day of each month, a senior man's haircut is $7.49 – equal to approximately 30 per cent off.)
- 12, 13160 – 118 Avenue; 414-0212 (60-plus)
- 6815 – 177 Street; 481-1360 (65-plus)
- 13127 – 82 Street; 472-2125 (60-plus)
- 14053 Victoria Trail; 476-1795 (senior cut $11.94 and senior shampoo & set $13.70 every day; 65-plus)
- 15827 – 87 Avenue; 484-8347 (60-plus)
- 5826 Terrace Road; 461-6008 (60-plus)

SALON – SHERWOOD PARK

- 17 Sioux Road; 467-4610 (60-plus)

SALON – ST. ALBERT

- 108, 398 St. Albert Road; 418-7626 (60-plus)

Hairdressing School Hair Salons

Why not consider giving a student studying hairstyling an opportunity to learn and get great senior discount pricing at the same time? Good deals on haircuts, shampoos and sets, perms and colours are commonplace at beauty schools but they take it a step further for seniors, providing a discount on their already-low prices. The students are under professional supervision at all times.

Estelle Academy of Hair Design
10469 – 80 Avenue in Edmonton; 432-7577
SAVE Senior customers save $1 off cuts and 10 per cent off colours every Thursday.
Age Requirement: 65-plus

Marvel College
10018 – 106 Street in Edmonton; 429-4407
SAVE 10 per cent off services for senior customers, every day.
Age Requirement: 65-plus

188 Seniors Save Money All Year Around

Barber Shops

Gentlemen! Time for a clip? Here are quite a number of barber shops who give senior pricing on haircuts. The qualifying age for the discount is noted below. Many barber shops are closed on Sundays and Mondays, so check beforehand. Most are on a drop-in basis for haircuts, although some will take appointments.

BARBER SHOPS – EDMONTON

Age Requirement: 55-plus
- Park Plaza Barber Shop, 11836A – 103 Street, 479-6505

Age Requirement: 60-plus
- Abbe's Barber Shop, Entrance #8 at West Edmonton Mall, 444-4763
- Sweeny Todd's Barber Stylists, 11011A – 107 Avenue, 426-2766

Age Requirement: 65-plus
- Gold Bar Barber Shop, 5028 – 106 Avenue, 469-7518
- Landsdowne Barber Salon, 5124 – 122 Street; 435-4333
- Larre's Barber Shop, 10325 – 124 Street, 488-3761
- Lendrum Barber Shop, 5834 – 111 Street, 434-1720
- Lynnwood Barber Shop, 15004 – 87 Avenue, 489-5911
- MB's Barber Shop, 8632 – 118 Avenue, 477-8937
- Primo & Tony's Barber Shop, 15613 Stony Plain Road, 489-1510
- Petrolia Barber Shop & Hairstyling, 114 Street & 40 Avenue, 434-5223
- Stan's Barber Shop, 11743 – 94 Street, 477-7498
- Telly's Barber Shop & Hairstyling Ltd., 7121 – 101 Avenue, 440-0805
- Universal Barber Shop, 10109 – 82 Avenue, 439-1203
- XL Barber Shop, 7604 – 112 Street, 436-0175
- Holyrood Barber Shop, 9012 – 75 Street, 465-5924

BARBER SHOPS – SHERWOOD PARK

Gene & Harry's Barber Shop, 48 Athabascan Avenue, 467-6111 (65-plus)

BARBER SHOPS – ST. ALBERT

The Barber Shop, 120 – 8 Perron Street, 458-0294 (65-plus)

Chapter 13

The Internet: Bargains, Electronic Newspapers and Newsletters, and Free Information

The Power of the Internet

It's no secret that today's seniors are a pretty computer-savvy bunch! Surfing the "world wide web" and utilizing email to communicate with friends and family have, in some instances, become a commonplace of daily life.

Being able to utilize the internet is handy because most businesses, services and associations have websites you can access at your convenience from home if you have a computer and an internet connection.

If you know how to navigate the world wide web, you can benefit from bargains in many areas such as travel, books and clothing as long as you feel comfortable ordering a product or service online (some people may be concerned about security). There is also access to free newsletters sent to you by email and opportunities to print out savings coupons in some instances. You may want to regularly access events calendars to see what's coming up in theatre or concerts, which is also something you can do online. The following are a list of useful websites.

Specifically for seniors:

- www.elderweb.org (Grant MacEwan College Elder Web – an online community of older adult computer users)

Travel:

- www.seniorsgotravel.com (*Edmonton Senior* newspaper)
- www.edmontonairports.com (Edmonton Airports: departure/arrival information)
- www.ppt.gc.ca (Government of Canada: passport information)
- www.cheaptickets.com
- www.expedia.ca
- www.travelocity.ca
- www.skyauction.com
- www.passages.gc.ca (Government of Canada: information on travel at home and abroad)
- www.50more.ca (information on senior travel)
- www.travelcounsel.com (Travel Counsel of Canada)
- www.womenwelcomewomen.org.uk
- www.TravelAlberta.com (Government of Alberta)

Event/Entertainment Listings in Edmonton & Area:

- www.winspearcentre.com (Edmonton's Winspear Centre For Music)
- www.jubileeauditorium.com (Edmonton's Northern Alberta Jubilee Auditorium)

International Calling Codes:

- www.countrycallingcodes.com

World Clock/Time Zones:

- www.timeanddate.com

Currency Converters:

- www.bankofcanada.ca/en/rates/
- www.xe.com

Language Translator:

- www.worldlingo.com

Weather:

- www.theweathernetwork.com (current and long-term weather forecasts for Canada)

Shopping:
- www.hbc.com (website access to DealsOutlet.ca)
- www.redflagdeals.com
- www.ebay.ca
- www.ebay.com
- www.pricenetwork.ca
- www.frugalshopper.ca
- www.save.ca (coupon site)

Auctions
- www.auctions.yahoo.com

Nutrition Information and Recipes:
- www.dieticiansofcanada.com (Dieticians of Canada)
- www.albertabarley.com
- www.albertapork.com
- www.growingalberta.com
- www.albertafarmfresh.com
- www.albertabeef.org
- www.chicken.ab.ca
- www.albertalamb.com
- www.eggs.ca
- www.campbellkitchen.com (Campbell's soup)
- www.crisco.com
- www.kelloggs.com/company
- www.recipeland.com
- www.recipesource.com
- www.cooks.com
- www.hersheys.com (Hershey's Chocolate)

Books
- www.alibris.com (50 million rare, used, new and out-of-print books; American)
- www.chapters.indigo.ca (Canadian)

Greeting Card Companies
- www.carltoncards.com (Carlton Cards)
- www.hallmark.com (Hallmark Cards)

Movies
- www.allianceatlantisfilms.com

Life Expectancy Calculator
- www.livingto100.com

Government (Senior-related)
- www.hrdc-drhc.gc.ca (Government of Canada – Pensions)

Health
- www.healthyalberta.com (Healthy U Alberta Program)
- www.ab.bluecross.ca (Alberta Blue Cross)
- www.health.gov.ab.ca (Government of Alberta Health & Wellness)
- www.hopkinsafter50.com (John Hopkins Medical Centre)

Genealogy
- www.lac-bac.gc.ca (Library and Archives Canada)

Driving Directions
- www.mapquest.com

Address & Phone Numbers in Canada
- www.canada411.com

E-Magazine & E-Newsletters
- www.chatelaine.com
- www.rona.ca (RONA Building Centre bulletins)
- www.homebasic.ca
- www.dairygoodness.ca

Pets
- www.pets.ca

Free Stuff!
- www.canadianfreestuff.com

Chapter 14

Your Home & Yard

This chapter has been broken down into the following categories:
- Inside your home;
- Outside your home;
- Painting your home;
- Locksmith services;
- Yard services;
- Home insurance;
- Energy savings; and
- Reusing/recycling.

Listed are many businesses and services that offer senior discounts, ranging from plumbers to lawn service companies. When choosing a business that provides services such as carpet cleaning, furnace repair, fumigation, plumbing or yard care, it's a good idea to ask friends and neighbours for recommendations.

In the Edmonton & Area telephone directory are some SuperPages coupons for great savings, from companies such as *A1 Rooter Plumbing & Heating Ltd., Able Furnace Cleaners, Acclaimed Furnace Cleaning, Allcolour Holloway Paints, Appliance All Service, ChemDry Express, Consumer Care Maids, Dominion Carpet Cleaning, J & L Appliances and Quicker Rooter Plumbing & Heating.* Note that these SuperPages coupons have expiry dates and that you will need to present the coupon to qualify for the savings. Also, advertisers and their offers can change from year to year. If you check the St. Albert, Spruce Grove & Stony Plain telephone directory, you will find a SuperPages coupon for **Dominion Carpet Cleaning.** There is a SuperPages coupon for *T & T Carpet Cleaning & Upholstery Care* in the Leduc & Area telephone directory.

Each year there are several major consumer shows that pertain to your home and yard. Admission for seniors is generally $2 to $3 less than the general admission. You can get some great ideas, enter free draws, and bring home free brochures and literature. Such shows include:

- *Edmonton Fall Home & Interior Design Show* (Edmonton Northlands; annually in September)
- *Edmonton Home and Garden Show* (Edmonton Northlands; annually in March)
- *Edmonton Renovation Show* (Edmonton Northlands; annually in January)

Are you an Air Miles collector? If you are undertaking some home renovations or repairs or building a fence, you may want to go to **Rona Home Centre** or **Totem Building Supply** stores as these are Air Mile sponsors.

Are you an AMA member? The "Show Your Card and Save Program" enables you to get savings at the following merchants: **Cloverdale Paint** and **Creative Door (Garage) Services.**

INSIDE YOUR HOME

Carpet Cleaning

The following companies are senior friendly and offer discounts, as mentioned in their yellow page advertising. You will need to enquire about the eligibility age for these senior discounts. Their names and telephone numbers follow, along with the offer indicated in their advertisement:

Some advertisements in the yellow pages under "Carpet and Rug Cleaners" indicate that if you mention their advertisement, you will receive a discount – so take a look. Some carpet cleaning companies offer good savings in the coupon books that are delivered to your home.

- *Advanced Furnace & Carpet Cleaning*, 434-7108 ("Seniors' discount").
- *Allied Carpet Care*, 433-4750 ("10 per cent senior discount" and note that they also clean furniture and offer pet disinfecting/odour control plus water and smoke restoration).
- *A-One Steamagic*, 437-1136 ("Senior discount" and note that they also offer odour control and flood/sewer backup cleanup).
- *ChemDry Select*, 460-2810 ("Senior discount" and note that they also offer a pet urine removal treatment, leather cleaning/repair and upholstery cleaning and that they serve St. Albert, Spruce Grove and Stony Plain).
- *T & T Carpet & Upholstery Care*; 980-2193 in Leduc ("10 per cent seniors' discount").

Appliance Service

Dishwasher not working? Washing machine making strange noises? There are a number of appliance repair companies that mention senior discounts in their yellow page advertisements. You will need to check with them directly about the eligibility age for the discount and ask whether the discount is on parts, labour or both.

- *AA Appliance*; north and west phone 473-8414; and south and east phone 434-8509 ("Save 10 per cent by mentioning this yellow page advertisement"; note that this company services Edmonton, Sherwood Park, St. Albert and Spruce Grove).
- *Able Appliance Service*; 461-4103 ("seniors' discount").
- *Accurate Appliance Services*; Riverbend and west end phone 484-6511, Clareview, northside, Castle Downs and St. Albert phone 421-4421 and southside and Millwoods phone 421-4209 ("15 per cent discount on labour to seniors").
- *Alberta Appliance & Refrigeration Service*; north Edmonton and St. Albert phone 455-1113, southside and Millwoods phone 468-5540 and west and downtown phone 482-4187

– note that this company services Edmonton and area ("Seniors' discount").

• *All Appliance Service*; 478-9895 ("Seniors' discount"; note that this company services Edmonton, Sherwood Park, St. Albert and Spruce Grove).

• *Appliance General Service & Repair*; 499-4240 ("Seniors' discount"; note that this company services Edmonton and St. Albert).

• *APTCO Appliance Sales & Service*; 471-2585 ("Seniors' discount available").

• *City Appliance and Refrigeration Service*; north and east phone 476-4629; and south and west phone 463-7733 ("10 per cent discount on labour to seniors who mention this yellow page advertisement").

• *Crown Appliance & Refrigeration Service*; north and east call 456-8001; and south and west phone 462-0900 ("15 per cent senior discount on labour"; note that this company services Edmonton, Sherwood Park, St. Albert, Spruce Grove, Stony Plain and Leduc)

• *Dial An Applianceman*; 473-4767 ("15 per cent discount on labour for seniors").

• *J & M Appliances Service & Repair*; 463-6401 ("10 per cent discount on labour for seniors").

• *Southside Appliances*; 432-3931 ("Senior discounts").

Appliance Parts

• *Metro Appliance Supply & Home Centre*; 478-1554 (Seniors' discounts, some restrictions apply").

Furnace Sales and Service

The following companies are senior friendly and offer discounts, as mentioned in their yellow page advertising. You will need to enquire about the eligibility age for the discount. Their names and telephone numbers follow, along with the offer indicated in their advertisement.

• Four Seasons Furnace, 438-2900 ("Seniors' discounts").

• Rob's Plumbing, 462-6833 ("Senior discounts").

Furnace Cleaning

The yellow page advertisement for *Advanced Furnace & Carpet Cleaning* (434-7108) indicates that they offer a "seniors' discount" on their furnace cleaning service.

Plumbing Service

Drip, drip, drip... that leaky tap! Problem with your garburator, toilet or hot water heater? There are a number of plumbing companies that mention senior discounts in their yellow page advertisements. You will need to check with them directly about the eligibility age for the discount and to determine whether the discount is on parts, labour, or both.

- *AAA Advanced Plumbing & Heating*; 446-0826 ("Seniors' discount").
- *ABA Plumbing & Heating*; 489-5415 ("10 per cent discount for seniors").
- *Accura Plumbing Ltd.*; 490-4902 ("Seniors' discounts").
- *Action Auger Canada Inc.*; in Edmonton phone 426-7704 and in Leduc phone 980-2500 – note that they service Edmonton and surrounding communities ("Seniors' discount").
- *Alberta Drain Cleaners* (1977) Ltd.; 475-5400 ("Discount to seniors").
- *All Star Plumbing, Heating & Drain Cleaning Mechanical Ltd.;* 438-3338 ("Seniors' discount: 15 per cent off on service jobs").
- *A Pro Solutions*; 453-6640 ("Senior citizen discounts").
- *Archie's Plu mbing & Drain Cleaning*; north phone 457-1898 and south phone 443-1453 ("Seniors' discounts").
- *Bauman Plumbing & Gasfitting Ltd.*; 414-1575 ("Seniors' discount").
- *Budget Plumbing & Heating 2000 Ltd.*; 433-1839 ("Seniors' discount"; note that they service Edmonton and Sherwood Park).
- *Dollarwise Plumbing, Heating & Drain Cleaning Ltd.*; 444-1166 (20 per cent off for seniors 55-plus).

- *Edmonton Drain Cleaners*; 424-1292 ("Discount to senior citizens").
- *Fast Rooter Plumbing & Heating*; 944-0734 ("Seniors' discount"; note that they service Edmonton and surrounding communities).
- *Professor Plumb Plumbing & Drain Cleaning*; 220-7586 ("seniors' discount").
- *Rob's Plumbing*; 462-6833 ("Senior discounts").
- *RRR Plumbing & Gasfitting*; 460-6851 ("10 per cent discount for seniors"; note that they service north Edmonton and St. Albert).
- *Service Pro*; 777-9556 ("Senior discount").

Electrical Service

The following companies are senior friendly and offer discounts, as mentioned in their yellow page advertising. You will need to enquire about eligibility age for the discount. Their names and telephone numbers follow, along with the offer indicated in their advertisement:

- *Allied Electrical Installations Ltd.*; 454-2738 ("Senior discount applicable").
- *Pannu Electrical & Control*, 707-4252 ("10 per cent seniors' discount on labour").
- *Sinclair Electric Ltd.*, 433-3112 ("10 per cent seniors' discount").

House Cleaning

The Edmonton company *Two To Clean* offers a discount for seniors. Their telephone number is 476-4883. They clean homes, apartments and condominiums and are bonded and insured.

Ray's Golden Touch Team offers a seniors' discount. Their telephone number is 484-9311. They clean homes, apartments and condominiums and are licensed, bonded, insured and police screened. See the listing for them in this chapter under "yard care" as they also provide that type of service to homeowners.

Exterminators/Fumigators

The following companies are senior friendly and offer discounts, as mentioned in their yellow page advertising. You will need to enquire about the eligibility for the discount. Their names and telephone numbers follow, along with the offer indicated in their advertisement:

- *Aardvark Pest Control Services*, 469-9904 ("Seniors' discount").
- *Academy Pest Control Ltd.*, 413-0409 ("Seniors' discount").
- *Dominion Crown Pest Control Services*, 460-2088 ("Seniors' discount").
- *Ecopest Inc.*, 448-2661 ("Seniors' discount").
- *Getz Rid Pest Control*, 906-4324 ("Senior discounts").

Fireplace/Chimney Cleaning

Chim-Chimney Ltd.
Telephone: 481-4147
SAVE Senior customers receive the company's "coupon discount" rate (anytime and no coupon necessary).
Age Requirement: 65-plus

Antique Furniture Refinishing

Lo-Cost Antique Refinishing
11625 – 147 Street; 432-1479
INFORMATION Services offered include stripping, repair and re-finishing and they have antique hardware in stock. They refinish furniture, pianos and cabinets and re-cane chairs.
SAVE Their yellow page advertisement indicates that they offer a discount to seniors.

OUTSIDE YOUR HOME

Snow Removal

The Edmonton company *Snow Crew* (435-3309) offers seniors' discount on their services (residential snow removal and roof top snow removal). Another Edmonton company, *Dave the*

Roofer (915-6737), also offers senior discounts on rooftop snow removal

Roofing

Dave the Roofer also offers senior discounts on re-roofing services. Their telephone number is 915-6737.

Foundation Repairs

Abarent Construction Ltd. of Edmonton (448-2592) specializes in foundation repairs (seepage problems, window wells, weeping tiles and structural repairs, etc.) and offers seniors' discounts.

Window Cleaning

The Edmonton company *Excellent Window Cleaning* (920-5587) offers year-round residential window cleaning, and also does eavestrough cleaning. They offer a seniors' discount.

Home Security Glass Laminate Suppliers/Home Security Systems

Home security systems offer peace of mind. Check with your agent for your house insurance. You can, in many instances, save money on the cost of your home insurance policy if you have a security system installed. Check with your agent.

The following companies offer senior discounts to customers (check with them on the age requirement to obtain the discount).

- *ACE Clear Defense*; 452-9977 ("Seniors' discount).
- *Bolt Security Systems*; 454-5864 ("Discount for seniors").
- *Border Security Systems*; 472-7700 ("Discount for seniors").

Sewer/Drain Cleaning

- *Action Sewer & Drain Cleaning*; 499-0766 ("20 per cent discount for seniors").

Painting Your Home

Perhaps the rooms in your home could use a fresh coat of paint? Or is it time to consider re-painting the exterior this year?

Yellow page advertisements for the following nine companies (listed under "Painters") indicate that they offer a senior discount, a senior rate or a winter booking rate. You will need to ask about the age requirement to qualify for the discount or senior rate.

Because the variables of house painting depend to such a large extent on your personal requirements (exterior versus interior; whole house interior versus one room or one level interior), you will need to work on estimates with these companies directly.

All the following companies offer services in interior and exterior painting except *Boone's Painting & Decorating, The Repaint Specialists Edmonton Inc.* and *Solid Rock Contracting,* which specialize in interior painting only.

- *Bliss Design and Decorating;* 709-4813 ("senior discount").
- *Colour View Painting;* 668-0650 ("special rates for seniors").
- *Consumer Painting & Construction Ltd.;* 721-6612 ("senior discount").
- *Dan's Painting Ltd.;* 913-7913 (10 per cent "senior discount").
- *Five Star Enterprises Inc.;* 444-7705 ("senior discount").
- *Karol's Master Painting Ltd.;* 479-6417 ("senior discount").
- *The Repaint Specialists Edmonton Inc.;* (10 per cent "senior discount").
- *Solid Rock Contracting;* 709-9739 ("senior discount").
- *Urban Painting;* 913-6010 (15 per cent off winter bookings).

Days Paint and Wallpaper

SAVE Seniors get a 10 per cent discount every day on purchases of paint, wallpaper, etc.

Age Requirement: 65-plus

LOCATED IN EDMONTON

- 10733 – 104 Avenue; 426-4848
- 3821 – 99 Street; 462-7720

• 382 St. Albert Road; 460-7708

ICI Paints and Wallpaper
• 9715 – 172 Street; 452-0141

SAVE Seniors receive a 10 per cent discount on purchases, every day.
Age Requirement: 65-plus

Locksmith Services

Are you considering installing deadbolts? Do your locks need re-keying? Do you need to cut new keys? The yellow page advertisements for the following three following Edmonton-based companies indicate that they offer a seniors' discount:
• *Ever Ready Locksmiths;* 478-1570
• *Master Locksmiths Ltd.;* 474-9011
• *Western Lock & Key;* 436-9077

YARD SERVICES

Trees

Jobs like tree removal, moving, topping, trimming, power-line pruning or stump removal are best left to a professional. All reputable companies are fully insured and will provide a free, no-obligation estimate.

The following companies offer senior discounts in their yellow page advertisements. You will need to ask about the eligibility age for the discount. Some tree companies also offer a "winter discount," and they are also listed here. Some offer both a senior discount and a winter discount – compare to see which discount is the better of the two.
• *AAA Arbor Kings;* west and south Edmonton 433-2722; and north and east Edmonton 471-5278 ("Senior discounts").
• *A-Able Tree Services;* 479-8996 ("Senior discount" and "winter rates").
• *Active Tree Services;* 479-6074 ("Seniors' discounts" and "winter rates").

- *Advanced Tree Service*; 471-0950 ("Senior discount" and "winter rates").
- *Alberta Arborists*; 448-0584 ("Senior discounts").
- *All Season Tree Service*; 464-2436 ("Seniors' discounts").
- *Arbor Care Tree Service Ltd.*; 413-9319 ("Winter discounts").
- *Arbor Man Tree Care*; 464-1728 ("Winter rates").
- *Big Tree Service*; 974-5618 ("Seniors' discount" and "Winter rates").
- *Stump ENS*; 968-0429 ("10 per cent seniors' discount").
- *The Tree Trimmer*; 413-0678; ("Winter discount").
- *University Arbor Services*; central and north Edmonton 455-4127; and southside 430-4799 ("Senior discount").

Greenhouses

Salisbury Greenhouses
- Sherwood Park; 467-5743

SAVE Senior discount of 10 per cent (with ID) on regular-priced merchandise, always.

INFORMATION Open year-round including Christmas greenery and poinsettias.

Age Requirement: 65-plus

Landscaping Services/Yard Care

Considering weekly maintenance on your lawn? A spring or fall cleanup? These three companies offer senior discounts in their yellow page advertisements. You will need to ask about the eligibility age for the discount.

- *Big R Gardening & Landscaping Ltd.*; 444-5107 ("Seniors' discount").
- *Ray's Golden Touch Team*; 484-9311 ("Seniors' discount").
- *Surely Green*; 417-0015 ("10 per cent off for seniors").

Lawn Care

Green Drop Lawns
www.greendrop.com
447-1000 in Edmonton

SAVE This company provides application of seasonally-blended fertilizer to improve lawn health plus aeration, pruning and tree/shrub service. Senior customers receive a five per cent discount. Another way to save is through the pre-pay option on five lawn applications throughout the season, which provides a savings of eight per cent.
Age Requirement: 60-plus for the senior discount; Anyone for the pre-pay discount.

Lawnmower Repair

The Lawnmower Hospital
    7555 – 72 A Street; 437-1851
SAVE Senior discount on lawnmower repairs offered. This shop services all makes and models. Pick-up and delivery service available.
Age Requirement: 65-plus

Insect, Weed and Tree Spraying

The following companies are senior friendly and offer discounts, as mentioned in their yellow page advertising. You will need to enquire about the eligibility age for their senior discounts. Their names and telephone numbers follow, along with the offer indicated in their advertisement:

- *Aardvark Pest Control Services*, 469-9904 ("Seniors' discount").
- *Academy Pest Control Ltd.*, 413-0409 ("Seniors' discount").
- *Dominion Crown Pest Control Services*, 460-2088 ("Seniors' discount").
- *Ecopest Inc.*, 448-2661 ("Seniors' discount").
- *Getz Rid Pest Control*, 906-4324 ("Senior discounts").

Home Insurance

There is too much diversity in this area for it to be possible to list companies providing some type of savings on policies. House insurance policies are based on your individual needs. The best advice here is to check with your current agent to see if you qualify for any savings on your house insurance policy on the basis of any of these factors:

- Mortgage-free;
- Non-smokers;
- Mature owners; and/or
- No claims.

Energy Savings Information

The ATCO EnergySense website (www.atcoenergysense.com) has some great tips on how to save energy in your home. There are tips for spring and summer energy savings along with those for fall and winter.

Reusing and Recycling

Downsizing? The City of Edmonton has a website directory that contains information on over 230 charities, businesses and city services that reuse or recycle items in the Edmonton area. All you need to do is type in the name of your item and you will find a list of places that will take it. Many of the charities will arrange to have your items picked up at no cost to you.

Check the Reuse and Recycling Directory at the City of Edmonton website: www.edmonton.ca.

Chapter 15

Other Good Value for You

Senior Club Memberships

Belonging to a senior club provides good value. As a member, you benefit from belonging to interest groups, taking courses and attending dances, or going on outings! There are no senior discounts because – you guessed it – all the memberships are purchased by seniors!

CARP Memberships

CARP, which calls itself "Canada's Association For The Fifty-Plus'" has a nationwide membership. The mandate of this non-profit group based out of Toronto is to promote the rights and quality of life of mature Canadians. Membership is $19.95 per year (which includes your spouse or partner) and benefits include the opportunity to be part of Canada's largest 50-plus lobby group; group benefits and services, and comprehensive out-of-country medical insurance; CARP travel services; and savings on a wide range of products and services, including hotels and car rentals. Members also receive six issues per year of their *50-Plus Magazine*. Further information is available on their website at www.carp.ca and by telephone at (416) 363-8748. There is a CARP Chapter operating in Edmonton.

Good Times Magazine Subscriptions

Canadian seniors can subscribe to *Good Times* magazine published eleven times per year by Senior Publications Inc. out of Toronto. An annual subscription is $23.49 including GST. Canadian content includes nutrition articles, health, fashion and feature articles on Canadian destinations. Their toll-free subscription line is 1-800-465-8443 and their website address is www.goodtimes.ca.

Spectator Sports

Edmonton Eskimos
www.esks.com
INFORMATION Season is June to November. Venue: Commonwealth Stadium. Tickets through TicketMaster, 451-8000.
SAVE You can save on tickets by choosing either the budget seating, in the upper deck (adult category) with savings of approximately 40 per cent, or by going with a group and getting a group discount on tickets.

Edmonton Northlands Horse Racing
www.thehorsesatnorthlands.com
Edmonton Northlands Race Track, 78 Street and 115 Avenue; 471-8174
INFORMATION Both harness and thoroughbred racing are featured at Northlands Park from spring to late fall. It is free to get into the track area and parking is also free!
LOYALTY CLUB Present your "Spectrum Players Club" card (free to obtain at The Slots at Northlands Park, at the same location) to receive one point credited to your account for each dollar you wager (if you win or not); the card should be presented to the pari-mutuel teller or inserted into the self-serve wager machine when you make your wager. This loyalty program is explained in Chapter 2 *Entertainment* (Casinos: Northlands Spectrum).
Age Requirement: Anyone

Edmonton Oilers
www.edmontonoilers.com

INFORMATION Season is October to April. Venue: Rexall Place.
Tickets: 414-GOAL (414-4625).

SAVE You can save on tickets by choosing eight-game mini-paks
(up to 20 per cent off individual game prices) or go with a
group and get the group discount on tickets.
Age Requirement: Anyone

DVD and VHS Movie Rentals

Blockbuster Video
www.blockbuster.ca

SAVE No late fees on movies and games – so if you take an extra
day or two to return them, there is no charge.
Age Requirement: Anyone

There are 20 Blockbuster Video stores in Edmonton; two in
both Sherwood Park and St. Albert; and one each in both
Spruce Grove and Leduc.

Roger's Video
www.rogersvideo.com

SAVE Promotions that are always featured are the "Roger's Video
Top 5" and "Return It Fast For Cash." If you want to rent
one of the top five movie rentals and Roger's doesn't have
a copy in stock, you get a free rental credit. If you rent one
of the top five and return it by noon the following day, you
receive a $1 credit.

INFORMATION On the website, there is a great "fun and free"
link. You can access a site on the top movie rentals from
2000 to the present – great for movie trivia buffs. There is
also a contest link.
Age Requirement: Anyone

There are 12 Roger's Video stores in Edmonton, two in
Sherwood Park and one in the communities of St. Albert
and Spruce Grove.

Clothing and Housewares Liquidation Outlets, Warehouses, Discount Stores, Clearance Centres and Factory Outlet Stores

Note that information on second-hand stores is in Chapter 11. Many of the second-hand chains offer senior discounts or a "Seniors' Day."

There are stores in Edmonton and area that provide discounted merchandise, are factory-direct outlets or sell merchandise from store liquidations. Some of these stores sell "off season" merchandise, meaning that they may retail winter clothing in the spring months.

- *Red Apple Clearance Centre* (Clothing, housewares, some grocery)
- *Giant Tiger All Canadian Family Discount Store* (Clothing, housewares, giftware and grocery)
- *Payless Shoe Source* (Designer knock-off footwear)
- *The Shoe Company* (Warehouse pricing on footwear at an average of 30 per cent off for brand names; these stores are Air Mile sponsors and you can also enquire about their "Extra Discount Card" program where you can save $10, $20 or $50, based on the amount you've spent.)
- *Winners* ("Off-price" fashion and housewares store retailing fashions at 20 to 60 per cent off retail price as they buy overstock directly from designers and retailers)
- *HomeSense* (20 to 60 per cent less than regular retail pricing on housewares)
- *Wholesale Sports Inc.* (Hunting, fishing, camping, archery and sports optics)
- *Discount Flags Superstore*
- *Liquidation World* (An ever-changing variety of merchandise from store liquidations)
- *XS Wares* (Discounted housewares)
- *End of the Roll Carpets*
- *Brick Clearance Centre*
- *Marshall Discount Fabrics*
- *The Book Outlet* (Books up to 75 per cent off list price)
- *Hobby Lobby Superstore*

- *XS Cargo* (electronics, household)

Don't overlook bargains at weekend flea markets, garage sales and rummage sales.

Old Strathcona Group Walking Tours and Guided Historical Tours

Always wanted to learn about the history surrounding the Old Strathcona area on Edmonton's southside? You'll also enjoy the sights and sounds of Whyte Avenue and its shops! Call *Out and About Tours* for details at 437-4182 or 909-8687. The tours are very affordably-priced.

Brightnights Edmonton Winter Family Festival

An annual delight! For just $10 per family vehicle, you can drive through Canada's largest Christmas theme park at Hawrelak Park with 500-plus displays. This event is a fundraiser for Edmonton's School Lunch Program. Runs from late November to early January.

Rebuilding Batteries

You can save both money and the environment through having old rechargeable batteries rebuilt. These can be from your cordless phone, cordless drill, notebook computer, electric shaver or whatever other electronics you need to keep charged up. This can be done at any *Circuit City* (formerly Radio Shack); there are 14 stores in Edmonton, one in Sherwood Park/St. Albert/Spruce Grove and two in Leduc.

Save Big on Craft Supplies

Flyers from *Michaels the Crafts Store* regularly feature 40 per cent off coupons (for one regularly-priced item) and sometimes they feature a 50 per cent off coupon. They also regularly feature coupons for savings on framing. Stores also hold weekend craft demonstrations and "Make It and Take It" sessions. There are a number of these stores in Edmonton and area.

Stationery, Office and Computer Supplies

At any *Staples Business Depot,* you can enroll in the Staples Rewards Program; it is free to enroll. You will receive notice of exclusive offers and contests plus a quarterly rewards statement summarizing your purchases. Customers can earn "Dividends Rebates" of up to $60 per year on purchase totals (some product exceptions apply). Customers must spend $250 at Staples per quarter to earn a rebate. Dividends Rebate coupons can be spent like cash in Staples Business Depot stores. There are four stores in Edmonton and one each in Sherwood Park, St. Albert and Spruce Grove.

At *Island Ink Jet* kiosks in many major shopping centres, you can save by having your computer ink-jet cartridges refilled. Not only are you saving money, but you are "reusing," which is great for the environment. Personnel at Island Ink Jet can advise you as to how many times a cartridge can be refilled.

Senior-Friendly Moving and Relocation Company

A regular advertiser in the *Edmonton Senior* newspaper, *Sunshine Relocation Assistance & Services* in Edmonton offers:
• Assistance with all moving needs
• Disposal of unwanted items
• Cleaning services related to moving
• Handyman services related to moving

They are licensed/bonded, insured, police-screened and you can get a free consultation. Their telephone number is 475-2585.

Used Sports Equipment

In the market for equipment for hockey, golf, snow sports, baseball/softball or fitness? You can save money by buying second hand quality equipment. *Play It Again Sports* has a great selection of used sports equipment at their two stores (in Edmonton at 220 Manning Crossing and in Sherwood Park at 222 Baseline Road). They also retail new sports equipment. The company is introducing a "Rewards Program" based on purchases at their two stores and they can explain the program to you; it will be free to

join the "Rewards Program". You can also check their website at
www.playitagainsports.com

Two other shops that sell both used and new sports
equipment are *Allsports Replay* at 6835 – 83 Street in Edmonton
and *Sports Exchange* at 7430 – 99 Street in Edmonton.

Sears New Outlook Program

Sears offers an opportunity to join the "New Outlook"
Program, their benefit program for customers 50-plus. For $24.99
annually, you will receive over $1,000 in Sears savings coupons, a
New Outlook Magazine subscription, a $5 Sears Gift Card and free
use of their website. Call 1-800-265-3675 for further information
or enquire at any of their four stores in Edmonton (Bonnie Doon
Mall, Kingsway Garden Mall, West Edmonton Mall and Southgate
Shopping Centre).

Quilting

If you are a member of any recognized quilters' guild, you
will receive 10 per cent off purchases at *Earthly Goods*. This shop
is located in the Lendrum Shopping Centre at 5848 – 111 Street
in Edmonton. At *Cottons and More* at 8645 – 63 Avenue (also in
Edmonton), quilters' guild members receive a 10 per cent discount
on cut fabric.

In Closing

We hope that in reading this book, you have learnt about many businesses and services that offer senior discounts in Edmonton and area, and can thus make good use of them. We hope, too, that you have become familiar with some of the great loyalty programs and obtained new ideas about free activities and events; and have discovered other valuable information. Remember to refer to the book often because that is its intended purpose.

It is convenient to know ahead of time where you can obtain a senior discount. However, when in doubt, always remember to ask if there is one, whether you are having a meal, ordering tickets to a concert, or shopping at store. Also keep in mind that if a business or store does not currently offer a senior discount, they may in future if enough seniors ask about one.

Ordering additional books (they make great gifts!)

If you would like to order additional copies of this book, *Seniors Save Money All Year Around Through All Kinds of Discounts, Free Offers and Valuable Information For People 50+ in Edmonton and Area*, at $14.95 plus $3.95 for postage and handling (plus GST), call (780) 425-7463 or toll-free 1-866-425-3540 or go to www.albertasenior.com.

Other publications by Alberta Business Research Ltd.

- *A Guide to Healthy Living for People 50+ in Alberta* – 230 pages ($18.69)

- *Free Offers, Great Discounts & Deals, Money-Saving Tips and Helpful Hints for People 50+ in Alberta* – 210 pages ($14.95)
- *Free Offers, Great Discounts & Deals, Money-Saving Tips and Helpful Hints for People 50+ in B.C.* – 230 pages ($18.95)

For more information on these publications, or to order, call (780) 425-7463 or toll-free 1-866-425-3540 or go to www.albertasenior.com.

Additions for the next edition

Do you have any information on Edmonton & area senior discounts or free offers to include in the next issue of this book? We would be happy to receive it. All submissions will be considered for the next publication.

Send them to:
Alberta Business Research Ltd.
#200, 10621 – 100 Avenue
Edmonton, Alberta
Canada T5J 0B3

Email: abrnews@shaw.ca